AIDS & AFRICAN AMERICANS

A Guide for Substance Abuse, Sexuality, and Care

Dr. Pamela Blackwell Johnson, LPC

NCD Publishing

2

Dr. Pamela Blackwell Johnson, LPC, is available for lectures and consulting on working with African Americans with HIV/AIDS. Leave word at Dallas office below.

Note: The author has worked to ensure that all information in this book is reliable if used appropriately. As research and practice advance, however, therapeutic standards and information may change. For this reason and because human and mechanical errors sometimes occur, we recommend that readers follow the advice of a physician who is directly involved in their care or the care of the party in question.

Library of Congress Control Number: 00-091405
ISBN: 0-9679718-0-2

NCD PUBLISHING &
Nia Consulting & Development
P.O. Box 741594
Dallas, Texas 75374-1594
(972)494-9497
www.NCDPUBLISHING.COM
1-800-484-9410, security code# 4660

ACKNOWLEDGMENTS

This book is a compilation of knowledge and experience I've accumulated in more than 10 years of working with African Americans impacted by HIV or AIDS. A full list of acknowledgments would have to include the hundreds of clients that I have seen over the years. Some who are no longer with us, some who continue to struggle, and many who are learning how to live successfully with HIV or AIDS.

It is from these individuals that I have learned far more, than they could possibly have learned from me. It is from these clients that I have grown, matured, and developed, not only as a therapist, but as a human being.

I am particularly grateful for the friendship and assistance I received from Cheryl Smith, Merriel Smith, and Glen Grace. Special thanks go to my family, friends and colleagues who have been supportive and understanding of all of my endeavors, especially, Nathan and Evan.

About the Author

Dr. Pamela Blackwell Johnson is a skilled and Licensed Professional Counselor with more than 10 years experience as a practitioner, researcher, and educator. She has counseled African American persons infected with HIV and/or AIDS since the epidemic began to significantly impact the African American community.

As a therapist, Dr. Blackwell Johnson has successfully facilitated individual psycho-therapy, crises intervention, family therapy and group therapy for these individuals and their loved ones. As a researcher, she has written and published African American Homosexual/Bisexual Males and HIV/AIDS: A Study of Racial Identity and Health Care Attribution.

She has developed two therapeutic models for counseling African Americans with HIV/AIDS. These include The Holland-Blackwell Model of HIV/AIDS Counseling Intervention and the Holistic Model for Counseling African Americans.

As an educator, Dr. Blackwell Johnson is Associate Professor at Amber University, teaching counseling and human development courses. She has long advocated the need for cultural sensitivity training and practice for mental health professionals. She has trained and lectured thousands of HIV/AIDS related professionals such as case workers, agency staff, mental health professionals, and the general public. She has shared her expertise and knowledge at many conferences, work-shops, and with the media.

TABLE OF CONTENTS

PART IV : HOLISTIC MODEL FOR A BETTER QUALITY OF LIFE ...189

Introduction

INTRODUCTION

My colleagues, students and friends have often asked, "What made you want to specialize in counseling individuals infected with HIV or AIDS?" I remember the first time I had to answer that question. It took me a few minutes to figure out what the answer truly was. You see, I never really planned to work with that population. It just kind of happened. I believe that I was just following God's lead and this is what He wanted me to do.

In 1990, I was a doctoral student at East Texas State University, in Commerce, Texas. It was time for me to decide on where I was going to work in order to fulfill my doctoral internship requirements. I went to my internship advisor at the university for help. She asked me what my interests were and did I have any preferences. All I knew was that I wanted to work with the African American Community.

She gave me a few people to contact in the Dallas area, but didn't have any solid leads into places that were predominately African American. Then she asked me if I had any "problems" with working with gay individuals. I told her I had never really thought about it, but that I certainly didn't mind trying. She said she didn't know if they had many African American clients, but there was a predominately gay agency that she had sent students to in the past, and had good results.

So it was at Oaklawn Community Services (OLCS) in Dallas, Texas, that my journey and my counseling career began. OLCS was a non-profit agency that catered to the gay community, and at that time the majority of their clientele was White. Because OLCS was geared to help the gay population, it was one of the few places that was experienced and designed to work with clients that had HIV/AIDS.

At this same time, African Americans were becoming infected with HIV/AIDS more and more, and therefore seeking HIV/AIDS services at OLCS. OLCS was rapidly beginning to have a large African American clientele. What I found at OLCS was a group of caring professionals who, unfortunately, had very little experience or insight into the African American community, client, and culture. Therefore these professionals were somewhat limited as to how they were able to help. I also found a very angry, discouraged and frightened group of African American clients who only wanted help, assistance, and care.

Somehow or another, my services were not only needed, but wanted. Although I was an intern, I provided a comfort level for many of the African American clients. I had some level of cultural knowledge and awareness, but more important I had a deeper level of sensitivity. Race was not the first thing that I noticed. It was their need, history, environment, and despair that I noticed first. It was through my insight into the cultural environment of this population that I was better able to assist these clients.

I am frequently reminded of an incident when one of the employees of the OLCS HIV/AIDS Day Center called upon me for assistance. The day center was a place for HIV/AIDS clients to spend the day for care, activities, food and other assistance. She said she had an African American male client that was "out of control," "raging," and if I didn't "do something with him" she was "going to call the police." She said that she feared he was "homicidal."

In my own "green counseling fear" I told her to send him to me. The client was indeed angry. He was talking loud and waving his hands. He talked about being "Black and treated poorly," he talked about having "AIDS," he talked about having "no where to live and no where to go," and he talked about "drugs and jail." He also talked about having "no money." But interestingly enough, I never saw him as "out of control." I never saw him as "homicidal." What she saw as "dangerous," I saw as "a brother being pissed-off." And my thoughts were...."for good reasons." More importantly, he was merely wanting someone to listen. He would not have hurt a fly.

It was at this time that I realized this was the right population for me to serve. I realized this population did not only include the African American clients, but also the people who chose to work with them.

Hence, the purpose in writing this book. It is my hope that any individual who chooses to work with the

African American HIV/AIDS related population, be it on a professional or non-professional basis, will try to learn more about that population from a cultural and sub-cultural perspective. Not that some of the points brought out in this book could not be seen in other races or cultures, but that these points are very often seen in African Americans with HIV/AIDS.

This book provides culturally specific guidance designed to help the infected population, their loved ones, and professionals. The information will help the readers gain better understanding, develop stronger levels of sensitivity, and learn tested approaches to helping this group of people. It will also guide the readers to a better quality of life for those infected and affected by the virus.

The needs for this book are threefold. First, historically, methods for counseling, case management, and other forms of emotional support for HIV or AIDS were developed using experiences and research conducted with gay, White Americans. Consequently, these methods are often inappropriate and culturally insensitive to many African Americans.

Second, the added issues of substance abuse and sexuality are often complex, overlapping and different from White Americans. For one to gain an effective approach to helping, they must acquire adequate information, understanding, and guidance when working on more than one of these problems at the same time. Third, because the rate of AIDS diagnoses is steadily increasing, the likelihood of more African Americans becoming impacted is escalating.

Therefore more professionals, friends, and families (African American and non-African American) are likely to become involved with a diagnosed African American in the years to come.

It is the aim of this book to give the readers a clear view of the sensitive and critical issues surrounding African Americans with HIV or AIDS, substance abuse, and sexuality. The primary purpose is to guide infected individuals and their caregivers to a better quality of life, empowering them to take responsibility for their own psychological health and well-being. I have tried to provide a holistic approach for helping, in culturally sensitive and effective ways.

Caregivers need to gain culturally specific insight as to how these issues affect African American individuals and the community-at-large. This information, if properly used, will help individuals develop appropriate methods for effective care.

It is my hope that regardless of the "helper's" color, profession, or requirements, they will gain some knowledge, awareness, and sensitivity that will help them to be the best care-giver they can be. It is also my hope that this book will provide some insight that might help encourage sensitive and effective quality of care.

<u>The Helper</u>:

For the purposes of this book the term "helper" is used to include all individuals who are impacting by someone with HIV/AIDS and who is trying to understand and assist them in some sort of way. The "helper" includes professionals, such as counselors, nurses, social workers, case-managers, staff, and doctors. The "helper" also includes non-professionals, such as volunteers, friends, family, co-workers, and church members.

<u>Case Story Names</u>:

All case story names are fictitious to protect the confidentiality of clients.

Part I:

In The Beginning

CHAPTER ONE

The African American AIDS Epidemic: The Impact and Causes

In the mid-1980s the Human Immunodeficiency Virus (HIV), which causes Acquired Immune Deficiency Syndrome (AIDS), quickly became a medical epidemic. Initially, this disease was thought to have primarily affected young, gay, White males. However, by the early 1990s, people of other ethnicities and/or races in the United States were diagnosed with this disease. Today, the largest of these groups is African American.

African Americans have also become the fastest growing group of newly diagnosed cases in the United States. According to the National Institute of Allergy and Infectious Diseases (NIAID), HIV and AIDS are still impacting the African American community at dispropor-tionate rates. In 1996, for the first time, the proportion of African Americans (41%) reported with AIDS surpassed

Whites. This figure is disproportionate because African Americans account for only 13% of the United States population (CDC, 1997).

RACE

AIDS is affecting more African Americans than any other minority group in the United States. In 1997, AIDS became the leading killer among African American men and women between the ages of 25 to 44. NIAID reported, for every 100,000 African Americans, there were approximately 89 AIDS reported cases in 1996. This figure is more than twice that of Hispanics (41) and six times higher than Whites (13).

The Centers for Disease Control and Prevention (CDC, 1999) determined that, of the AIDS cases reported during a 12-month period (July 1998-June 1999), the racial breakdown of the adults and adolescents was 20% Hispanic, 33% White, and 46 % African American. By June of 1999, the CDC reported over 36% of all of the AIDS reported cases were African American. The same report showed over 52% of the HIV infected cases (from 33 areas with confidential HIV infection reporting) were also African American.

GENDER

Compared to other major ethnicity-gender groups, the number of AIDS cases is growing fastest among African

American women. From July 1998-June 1999, women account for 23% of the reported adult AIDS cases. African American women account for 62 % of all current adult female AIDS cases, even though they only make up 13% of the adult female population (CDC, 1999). AIDS is now the leading cause of death among African American women ages 25-44 (Harmon, 1999). Of the female adult HIV infection cases reported from July 1998 to June 1999, over 68% were African American.

African American men also continue to be impacted by AIDS at alarming rates. From the period of July 1998 to June 1999, 41% of the adult male cases of AIDS reported were African American. During that same time period, 47% of the adult male cases of HIV reported were African American. Of the cumulative adult males reported with AIDS and HIV, 32% and 47%, respectively, were African American (CDC, 1999).

<u>YOUTH</u>

Because of the growing number of young people with HIV/AIDS, the future of African Americans is seriously at stake. Approximately 19% of the cumulative African American AIDS cases were from individuals who were under the age of 30. During the July 1998 to June 1999 period, 63% of the children under 13 with AIDS were African American. Of cumulative pediatric AIDS reported cases, 58% were African American (CDC, 1999).

DEATHS

From 1991 through 1996, over 93,200 African Americans with AIDS died. Of the total number of US AIDS related deaths, during this period, 35% were African American (CDC, 1997). Although there is no cure for this disease, AIDS education coupled with new medications has helped to reduce the rate of death and increase the length of HIV status. Many individuals with HIV/AIDS are living longer and healthier than ever before.

According to the CDC in 1997, AIDS related deaths declined 28% for Whites, but only 10% for African Americans. "Overall deaths decreased 42% from 1996 to 1997, and 30% from 1997 to 1998. The number of persons living with AIDS continues to increase. At the end of 1997, there were over 250,000 persons living with AIDS in the US. By the end of 1998, there were over 297,000 persons living with AIDS, a 10% increase," (CDC, 1998 & 1999). Since people are living longer with HIV and AIDS, the amount of time for those who are infected and still practicing risky behaviors is prolonged, thereby increasing the opportunity for continuing the spread of the disease.

THE PUBLIC'S RESPONSE

Over the past 15 years, HIV and AIDS have become topics of great interest, concern, and debate. HIV/AIDS was initially thought to have ravaged thousands of people, mostly gay White men, in very short periods of time. Otherwise healthy men were becoming very ill, suffering, and ultimately dying within just a few years, and some within months of their diagnosis. In the early years, HIV/AIDS literally kept diagnosed individuals from fighting infections or other diseases. This complicated the quality of treatment, medication, and emotional support.

Because of the vast devastation, much attention has been given to HIV and AIDS. Some of that attention has been positive, but at the same time much of that attention has been negative. In the early years, the negative attention began with anti-gay groups. The lifestyles and sexual behaviors of some of the diagnosed individuals were criticized and made to be more of an issue than the health and welfare of human beings. The media, including movies, books, and magazines, seemed to focus on the controversial topics that would sell their products. From this negative and often insensitive attention many myths, stereotypes, stigmas, and prejudicial fears developed among American people.

Fortunately, within the recent years, there was a significant shift, and much more positive attention began to appear. This attention included advanced research, improved medication and medical treatment, and increased funding and financial assistance. Along with physical advancements came improved public sensitivity and education, as well as effective emotional and psychological support. Through positive attention individuals with HIV and AIDS today have the potential to have longer and healthier lives.

Because HIV and AIDS was thought to have primarily begun in the gay White community, so did all of the above mentioned positive attention. In fact, effective AIDS education, prevention programs, and services in the gay community has helped to significantly reduce the rate of infection for gay White males. During the period of July 1996 to June 1997, there was a decline among new AIDS diagnoses. The declined was 13% among Whites and 5% among Hispanics, but 0% among African Americans.

WHY THE RAPID SPREAD?

The question is, "Why?" Why is the rate of infection decreasing faster in the White community than in the African American community? Why are there more African American women with AIDS than White women when the disease at one time was affecting primarily Whites? Why is the rate of AIDS related deaths higher in the African American community than in the White community when this disease at one time was affecting primarily White gay men?

Logically, it would be easy to say that HIV and AIDS in the African American community can be combated by simply repeating the same HIV and AIDS programs and services that worked for the gay White male community. Unfortunately, that thought is too simplistic and unrealistic when working with the African American community.

Research (Belgrave & Randolph, 1993) on the African American AIDS epidemic has primarily centered on certain psycho-social aspects in the African American community. These aspects include behavioral factors which tend to be the primary method of HIV transmission from one individual to another, and contributing factors which tend to be focal points of understanding some of the psycho-social causes for the continued spread of infection.

BEHAVIORAL FACTORS

There are certain groups of people, which, because of their behaviors, fall into what is called high-risk-of-infection behavior categories (Lester & Saxxon, 1988).

These categories include homosexual and bisexual males with and without histories of intravenous drug abuse, heterosexual intravenous drug abusers, heterosexual contacts of persons with AIDS or at increased risk for AIDS, persons with hemophilia and other blood coagulation disorders, recipients of blood to blood product transfusion, and persons with "no known risk" (pp. 565-566).

The significant implication to note is that a large percentage of African Americans fall into these high-risk-of-infection behavior categories, which increases the chances of contracting the virus (Lester & Saxxon, 1988).

Belgrave and Randolph (1993) reported that the rate of infection by these various exposure categories is also different for African American males than for their female counterpart.

EXPOSURE CATEGORIES

Similar to the gay White male population, the African American gay male was the hardest hit. However, unlike that of the White population, African American heterosexual persons are diagnosed with AIDS at alarming rates. From July 1998 to June 1999, 30% of the African American male adults and adolescents diagnosed with AIDS reported homosexual exposure, 26% reported exposure by intravenous (IV) drug use, and 11% reported exposure by heterosexual contact. Compared to the White counterpart during the same 12 month period, about 64% of the White men with AIDS reported having sex with other men, 12% reported intravenous drug use, and only 4% reported heterosexual contact (CDC, 1999).

Of the adult and adolescent African American women reporting an AIDS diagnosis in the same 12 month period, 26% reported exposure by IV drug usage and 38% reported exposure by heterosexual contact (CDC, 1999). Compared to the previous reports, African Americans infected with AIDS through heterosexual contact is increasing steadily.

Approximately 35% of the cumulative total of African American adult and adolescent males with AIDS and 43% of the cumulative total of African American adult and adolescent females with AIDS are cases reported from individuals who injected drugs. (CDC, 1999). This trend could be contributed to two basic factors:

> 1. It is important to understand that it is the poorer and less-educated drug abuser (who is more likely to be African American) who will probably share needles rather than buy new unused needles (Jue & Kain, 1989); and 2. African Americans usually share needles with other African Americans and often times these groups share family membership or have friendship bonds (Fullilove, 1989).

HOMOSEXUALITY

Traditionally, African Americans have shown great resistance to accepting homosexuality as a reality in their community. Consequently, African Americans have been reluctant in providing community based sensitivity and support for such individuals. For the most part, homosexuality has been "ignored, made fun of, or thought to be shameful."

One of the major differences in the way African American homosexuality seems to differ from that of White homosexuality is that the White gay community thinks of "gay" as being a part of one's life or lifestyle. Whereas, many African Americans seem to think of "gay" as having to do with primarily behaviors and more specifically, sexual behaviors.

<u>SECRETIVE LIVES</u>

Because homophobia is so common among many African Americans, "coming out" is not always a viable option. Many African American gay individuals have led a very secretive life that is often magnified due to fear of rejection and discrimination from their own family and friends.

These fears can lead to very secretive, inappropriate, and often promiscuous sexual partners and behaviors, thereby perpetuating the increased risk for HIV infection. In addition, these feelings have also led to increased substance abuse among gay African Americans, in an effort to avoid or "deal with" emotional pain.

Jue and Kain (1989) reported that many minority individuals express feelings of isolation. They stated:

> This lack of a large and viable gay minority community with which to identify and the difficulty minority men have in assuming a personal gay or bisexual identity result in a situation of severe isolation—not only from AIDS care but also from AIDS education. Whereas White gay men receive AIDS education information through gay newspapers, gay bars, and gay organizations, this information will not be readily available to most ethnic minority gay men.

BISEXUALITY

Homophobia has been internalized in the African American community for generations. Consequently, homophobia has perpetuated the avoidance, insensitivity, and ignorance of homosexuality issues among African American individuals. It is because of these "well kept secrets" that many African American men and women continue to live partly homosexual lives and partly heterosexual lives. Such dual lives could be helping to increase the rate of HIV infection to others (Dalton, 1989), including the heterosexual community, especially if they are having unprotected sex.

Jenkins, Lamar & Thompson-Crumble (1993) stated:

> Conservative sexual attitudes may contribute to the increased number of AIDS cases associated with bisexuality by promoting closet behaviors. Because many African Americans are taught that homosexuality is not indigenous to the Black community, many who are homosexual are pressured to maintain heterosexual relationships and those who are bisexual must keep the homosexual relationships discrete (pp. 117-118).

Bisexuality in the African American community is often considered a viable alternative "to being gay." Again, because of the shame and stigmatization of alternative sexual preference in the African American community, many African Americans choose to lead "two lives," one that is heterosexual with perhaps a spouse and children and one that is homosexual with perhaps a lover that he or she has in a secretive relationship.

Case Story:

Alex was a 50-year-old African American man who was a very successful businessman and a deacon at a very large urban church. Alex worked very hard to make his parents proud of his accomplishments.

Alex was also married and the father of three children. He admitted to trying all of his life to "fight the urges" of having sex with men. He said that he "truly tried not to be gay." He said that he didn't even want to admit to himself that he enjoyed being with men. He thought that having a wife and children would make a difference.

In the later years of his marriage, he stopped having sex with his wife in fear of exposing her to the virus. He and his wife had agreed to stay together for the "sake of the children." He still did not tell her about his sexuality nor did he tell her that he had HIV. His wife only suspected that her husband was having an affair with another woman. She never thought that he was having an affair with a man.

Only after he started to have medical problems did he tell her of his diagnosis. She was soon tested and also diagnosed with HIV.

Bisexuality can cause extremely complicated, stressful, and emotional situations for the AIDS-diagnosed person. The guilt and pain of disclosing one's sexual history or homosexual behaviors and thereby possibly exposing a partner to the virus can seem unbearable. Consequently, this individual may avoid telling the partner for dangerously long periods of time.

Case Story:

Cindy was a 31- year-old African American woman. She was faithful to her husband of six years when they began having marital problems. They soon separated and did not see each other for a few years.

Cindy did not hear from her husband until he was hospitalized with medical problems. She visited him at the hospital, only to find him on his death bed. Even so, he did not tell Cindy of his diagnosis.

It wasn't until her husband died that she found out he had AIDS. She and her children immediately became tested, only to find out that she had HIV.

After she disclosed her HIV status to some friends, she was told by one of them that they "heard" her husband was gay.

It is not uncommon for some individuals to be completely unaware that their partner is bisexual, only to find out after they are diagnosed with the virus.

DIRECT DRUG-RELATED BEHAVIOR

Because of historical oppression, discrimination, and subsequent depression, substance use and abuse has been a major coping mechanism for many African Americans. When the weight of emotional pain gets too heavy to carry, alcohol and drugs have often been used to "temporarily escape from the pain" or to help one to just "feel better."

Although direct IV drug usage is a major form of HIV transmission, it is not the only drug-related behavior that contributes to the spread of the disease. Other methods of substance abuse such as smoking and snorting cocaine, alcohol consumption, and the use of all other illegal drugs can lead to other risky behaviors, such as unprotected sex. Such risky behaviors can put an individual at a higher risk of contracting HIV.

When using any mind-altering substance, an individual tends to have an impaired sense of making sound judgments and healthy decisions. The use and/or abuse of drugs and alcohol may lead that person to risky sexual behaviors that are directly related to contracting the disease. Such behaviors include having promiscuous sex, unprotected sex or sex with improper use of condoms, inappropriate partner selection, and dangerous sexual practices.

Case Story:

Greg was a 40-year-old African American gay man who was also diagnosed with HIV. Greg was a quiet and somewhat introverted individual. He had accepted his homosexuality but his father's disapproval influenced Greg to remain a very private and often lonely person. Meeting and socializing with new people was very difficult for him until he had a drink or two. Greg said that after a few drinks he is much more relaxed and sociable, and more likely to have an intimate date with someone that he hardly knew.

INDIRECT DRUG-RELATED BEHAVIORS

Indirect drug-related behaviors can also increase an individual's risk for contracting the disease. Although an individual may not use drugs, there are indirect drug-related activities such as sex with drug users, sex for drugs, and sex for money to purchase drugs.

CONTRIBUTING FACTORS

In the African American community the AIDS epidemic has been attributed to a lack of understanding of AIDS (Lester & Saxxon, 1988). One source for the lack of understanding is the prevailing belief that AIDS is a disease associated with White gay men (Croteau, Nero, & Prosser, 1993; Mitchell, 1990). This stigma began in the early 1980's when many AIDS cases were found in otherwise healthy White American men who reported having a history of homosexuality.

MULTIPLE SUB-GROUPS

Contrary to the gay White male population, efforts for prevention and education in the African American community could not be targeted to just one exposure category, such as White male homosexuals. Initially, African Americans with HIV or AIDS were mostly gay men and people who had reported histories of IV drug usage. Because of the increased presence of IV drug-induced infection the exposure categories were also broadened into the heterosexual community. As with all people, but especially with African Americans, the issues are not just the sexual or drug-related behaviors of an individual, but also the entire history of that person's sexual or drug-related behaviors and that of their partners.

Many African Americans who are diagnosed with HIV are neither gay, nor IV drug users. African Americans with HIV/AIDS also include bisexual and heterosexual adults and children, many of whom were not promiscuous or were not considered to be in a high-risk-of-infection category.

In fact, many of these individuals could have been infected by either suspecting or unsuspecting carriers of the disease. Consequently, the profile for African Americans exposed to HIV or AIDS is very different from what America has seen in the past.

The majority of the White AIDS cases were in predominantly one exposure category, consequently, the population at risk and most impacted was easier to target and therefore easier to alarm and help. By contrast, in the

African American community, several exposure categories are common and therefore putting almost the entire African American community at risk.

For various reasons, such as homophobia and addiction, it is much easier to reach one or two groups within the White community than it is to reach African American gay individuals, African American bisexual individuals, and IV drug users. It is especially difficult to reach the heterosexual and non-drug related African American who does not think they are at risk. Couple these social issues with racism, poverty, and emotional pain only magnifies the epidemic.

Case Story:

Beatrice was a 19-year-old African American woman from a small town. Beatrice was a "good church girl," who had no interest in drugs or alcohol and had no sexual partners until her boyfriend Charles, who became her husband. They soon had one son.

Later, Beatrice and Charles began to have marital problems due to Charles' increasing interests in drugs and alcohol. At the age of 21, Beatrice thought she was pregnant and went to her doctor for confirmation. At the time she received positive pregnancy results she was also told that she was HIV-positive.

The problem at hand is that AIDS is no longer just a gay White man's disease, no longer just a gay disease, no longer a disease for mostly IV drug users, and no longer a disease for just those who have promiscuous sex. In addition to all of the above categories, AIDS is now a disease that almost anyone can contract. The statistics suggest that within the African American community the chances of contracting the disease are the highest.

Hence, one of the major causes for the increasing rate of infection is the difficulty in reaching everyone who needs to be reached with proper education and information. It is difficult to reach African American men who are secretly gay, or IV drug users who only care about using, or individuals who practice prostitution. It is difficult to target individuals who don't know that their mate has multiple sex partners.

It is difficult to target individuals who don't know their mate once used IV drugs. It is difficult to target individuals who don't know that their mate is bisexual. It is difficult to target individuals who still think it is a gay White disease. It is difficult to target individuals who simply "don't think it could happen to them."

SOCIO-ECONOMIC IMPLICATIONS

There seems to be a correlation between income and education levels when compared to health status (Goodwin, 1992; Fullilove, 1989). Approximately 84% of the reported AIDS cases were in metropolitan areas with 500,000 or more population. And approximately 10% of the reported AIDS cases were in metropolitan areas with 50,000 to 500,000 population (CDC, 1999). African Americans that reside in such areas are often victims of oppression and racism at such massive levels that their primary interests are basic survival issues such as employment, food, rent, and clothing.

In such cases preventive health care may not be considered as important as coping with stress, poverty, or unemployment. "When life is a day-to-day struggle to balance single parenting, unemployment or working two or three jobs, dealing with substandard education, lack of money, teen-age pregnancy and homelessness, all very present realities for many in the African American community, AIDS seems a distant specter" (Mitchell, 1990).

The end result is often depression or anger, which can lead to behaviors and practices such as drug addiction and high-risk-of-infection sexual activity. Consequently, those who are at a lower economic level and also practicing risky behaviors run an even higher risk of coming into contact with someone that has HIV or AIDS.

"IT'S A GAY, WHITE DISEASE"

Because HIV and AIDS was historically a disease thought to be mostly among gay White men, a serious and prevailing stigma developed among the rest of American society. African Americans, in particular, began to associate HIV and AIDS as a "gay White disease" and therefore did not seriously consider the implications and level of risk for the African American community. Many African Americans simply didn't think they were at risk.

Gay African American men did not start to accept the potential threat of HIV and AIDS until many gay African American men became diagnosed with AIDS and began to die. (Many of these individuals still thought it was a gay White disease.)

Case Story:

Robert was a very attractive 21-year-old African American gay man. He found out that he had HIV soon after his graduation from college. Robert admitted that he was promiscuous in college and just enjoyed "having a good time." Robert admitted that he was aware of HIV and had HIV education.

He continued by saying that none of his friends "seemed to have HIV," and he only knew of White individuals who had it. He said that he just "didn't think it would happen to him."

African American IV drug users also did not start to accept the potential threat of HIV and AIDS until many African American drug users became diagnosed and began to die. Many of these drug users still considered it to be a gay disease and did not identify with that segment of the population.

Case Story:

Martha was a 39-year-old African American woman who admitted to a history of prostitution and substance abuse. She said that she really didn't know much about

*AIDS because all she thought about was "getting loaded."
She says that she also didn't think she was at risk of contracting AIDS because she "didn't shoot-up" and she "did-
n't do gays." She said that she knew a lot of gays that were
dying of AIDS but "didn't think it would happen" to her.*

Additionally, African American heterosexual men
and women who did not necessarily display risky behaviors
were also becoming diagnosed at alarming rates. These
individuals also fell into the category of those who did not
think it would happen to them.

Case Story:
*Ann was a 66 year old African American grand-
mother. She says she never used any kind of drugs or alcohol, and never had promiscuous sex. She said that she knew
exactly who infected her with HIV because she only had sex
with one man for the past 15 years. Unfortunately she did
not know that her mate was also bisexual. He was unaware
that he had the disease. She simply "never thought it would
happen" to her.*

DENIAL

The mental state of denial is another major cause for
the rapid spread of AIDS in the African American community. The notion that "it won't happen to me," has been
detrimental to many individuals. It is unfortunate that 15
years ago, the United States was in denial about the serious
long-term implications resulting from hundreds and thou-

sands of gay White men dying from AIDS. It is unfortunate that African American gay men were also in denial about the risks of contracting AIDS, until hundreds of African American gay men began to die.

Much of the rest of the African American community was also in denial about the impact of AIDS, until hundreds of women, heterosexual men, teenagers and children began to get infected. Denial seems to be a major issue that exacerbates the problem of AIDS in the African American community. This denial exists with the infected and the non-infected individual, the families, the churches, the leaders and politicians, and the community at large. Many individuals had been in denial about the risk of contracting AIDS, until someone they knew became diagnosed.

The major problem with denial is that all of the AIDS education and information in the world sometimes is just not enough. An individual can know all of the facts, but if they still don't want to believe it can happen to them, or simply don't want to believe or think certain things about their partner, then what good are all of these facts?

HIV/AIDS PROGRAM AVAILABILITY

One primary source of the lack of understanding of AIDS and the increasing rates of infection is the scarcity of AIDS prevention and education programs in the African American community. Because AIDS was originally believed to be only a White gay man's disease, much of the HIV/AIDS funding, research, programs, and services were designed for and provided to the White gay community. Therefore, information was scarce regarding the medical, behavioral, and psychological implications of AIDS towards the non-White community, in general, and the African American community, in particular (Foster, Phillips, Belgrave, Randolph, and Braithwaite, 1993.) Foster et al. (1993) reported:

> Limited availability of AIDS-related programs and services is felt even more acutely in the African American community, where there is a disproportionately high occurrence of HIV infection and a disproportionately low occurrence of culturally relevant programs and resources (p. 124).

According to the CDC and the US Department of Health and Human Services, at a 1987 AIDS and Minorities Conference, a large percentage of the federal dollars were going to the ethnic-majority and bypassing the ethnic minorities (Foster et al., 1993). Even when HIV education is available many African Americans may not trust White educators and other professionals enough to seek the needed information and services.

INSTITUTIONAL RACISM AND DISCRIMINATION

Institutional racism and discrimination are not strangers to African Americans, especially with regard to health care and medical treatments. Historically, public health programs and facilities in the African American community have generated negative feelings (Jenkins et. al., 1993). During the early 1900s and even into the 1960s, such programs tried to "reduce fertility among African Americans," and used African Americans as subjects to study the "effect of untreated syphilis" (Jenkins et al., 1993, p. 115; Thomas & Quinn, 1991).

Due to discrimination, many African Americans receive inadequate medical and social care. Consequently, they may avoid seeking certain forms of assistance because of "the way that they may have been treated." And even in the facilities where the employees are not consciously being discriminatory, they may be ignorant and culturally insensitive to African Americans and, thereby, also providing discriminatory or ineffective care.

FUNDING

The few African American HIV/AIDS related agencies, clinics, and social service programs that do exist are having a difficult time getting adequate proportions of the HIV and AIDS funding that becomes available. Many of these African American AIDS related facilities are smaller with very little experience or political clout. Therefore, they are often overlooked or discriminated against by the larger, more established facilities or funding sources.

RESEARCH

Most of the HIV and AIDS research, theories, and techniques, in the past have been conducted on Whites. Therefore, African Americans have often received HIV and AIDS medical and social treatments, education, social services, and even funding based on information and research gathered on that population. Only recently have research efforts concentrated on the issues that are culturally specific to African Americans.

The issues of women and HIV are now also becoming topics of interest to researchers. In the past, even women were treated using the results found from studies conducted with male subjects.

HOW DID THE WHITE GAY COMMUNITY DEAL WITH IT?

Because the majority of HIV and AIDS cases were initially thought to have been in the White gay community and existing for a longer period of time, the long term effects of AIDS prevention and education began to work. AIDS funding, gay political power, "coming out," multiple deaths, and HIV/AIDS programs and services began to show positive results, but primarily for that community. The CDC (1999) reports that the rate of infection and death is going down faster for Whites than for minority groups.

GAY COMMUNITIES

Comparatively speaking, among the White gay population it is now common for major cities to have predominately gay communities. These communities include gay-owned and operated businesses, print and broadcast media outlets, social, psychological, and medical services and agencies, churches, and residential areas. The gay and predominantly White community has helped provide social, public, and emotional support to its members.

This mostly White gay community is also significant in helping individuals with a sense of pride, strength, identity, and esteem. With regard to HIV and AIDS, this gay community has been instrumental in providing HIV and AIDS education and prevention, HIV and AIDS social and medical support, and HIV and AIDS related political and economic power.

Unfortunately, in most African American communities, a gay sub-community does not often exist. Therefore, the African American gay person may not have the most effective education, support, services, and political power to help reduce the rates of increased infection, like that of the White counterpart.

EDUCATION AND PREVENTION

When thousands of gay White men became diagnosed with HIV and AIDS, the gay White community quickly began to fight back. Massive AIDS prevention and education programs were conducted in almost every corner of the community. Individuals were willingly and frequently receiving HIV testing and counseling.

Condoms were advertised and provided for in many of the gay public and private businesses. Pamphlets, brochures, and tapes were produced and distributed throughout the community. HIV and AIDS education classes were frequently conducted. All of these educational and preventive efforts contributed toward fighting the battle of the continued spread of HIV and AIDS.

AIDS FUNDING

Due to the epidemic proportions of the disease, sources of financial support began to develop and were distributed throughout the very much needed, predominantly White gay community. The money was dispersed to the various social and service programs, as well as medical facilities. These financial efforts also included assisting AIDS-diagnosed individuals with their personal monetary needs.

Funding from private grants, government grants, and national and local fund-raising projects began to increase year after year. It is primarily with adequate amounts of money that many of these HIV and AIDS programs and services were successful. Additionally, enhanced HIV and AIDS research was conducted, improving advances in medication and treatment.

GAY POLITICAL POWER

The political power of the White gay community is very well organized, productive, and growing stronger every year. It is with political power that AIDS-related legislation, policies, economic systems, and effective social changes began to occur. This political power also helped to improve the level of sensitivity to AIDS and the quality of the once adverse media coverage. It is due to this political power that the disease and gay civil rights began gaining stronger levels of public respect and legislation.

GAY PRIDE

The predominantly White gay community's willingness to disclose their sexual preference as a part of the gay pride movement was also significant in fighting the battle of HIV and AIDS. Gay pride movements, parades, advertisements, and conferences helped to build the gay political power and focus political attention to fight HIV and AIDS.

Gay White men began to disclose their HIV status to help other gay men and the general public with HIV testing and information. They also began to unite in various AIDS awareness and fund-raising projects. Because these gay men were not trying to hide their lifestyle, they were more apt to seek AIDS related services, including AIDS medical and psychological services, and AIDS related social services.

Gay White men and women were "coming out of the closet" because of their own personal reasons and also to help the fight against HIV and AIDS. "Coming out" also helped to get families and friends involved in the efforts of fighting HIV and AIDS.

MULTIPLE DEATHS

The most unfortunate but perhaps most significant contribution to the reduction of the rate of AIDS infection was the loss of so many lives. Within the gay White community, so many people died or became seriously ill that efforts to mobilize became crucial.

Whites and gays began to lose many of their friends as well as partners. Along with multiple deaths came multiple grieving. In memory of their deceased friends, gays and others impacted began to work even harder, volunteering their services, raising money, physically taking care of ill friends, and helping to protect themselves and others from further infections.

WHY HAS THIS NOT WORKED FOR AFRICAN AMERICANS?

The previously mentioned programs that worked in the gay White community have not had the same success with African Americans for several reasons. The first of which is the African American political power at large is still developing and growing, therefore African American gay political power is almost nonexistent. Little, if any, organized political and economic power has surfaced among African American gays and certainly not among drug users. In order to receive funding, political and social power is needed.

Second, in order to have such power, more and more African Americans, including African American gay men and women, will have to mobilize. Due to the pervasive levels of homophobia and the fear of rejection, "coming out of the closet" can be a very difficult and emotion endeavor for many African Americans to undertake. African American "gay pride" efforts are still struggling.

Without political power, access to funding is undermined, civil rights are frequently violated, and effective amounts of African American related services are limited. Without funds it is difficult to have adequate education, prevention, and treatment programs for the African American gay man and the African American community at large.

Third, the risk of African Americans contracting AIDS is not contained primarily to gays. Because of the large population of IV drug reported cases and reported cases through heterosexual contact, the entire African American community must become a major point of focus and must also mobilize.

Due to political and social disapproval, it is often difficult to get funding for needle exchange, condom distribution, and street outreach programs. It is also difficult to effectively persuade many African American men and women to practice safer sex.

Even the issue of multiple deaths has yet to have a significant impact on the African American community, primarily because of the prevailing feelings of shame or embarrassment that exist. Although many African Americans have died from AIDS, their families remained secretive and avoided disclosing or discussing the cause of death.

CHAPTER TWO

Cultural Commonalities Among African Americans

Over the past decade, the word "culture" has become a new buzz-word in almost every facet of American society. Corporate culture, cultural diversity, cultural standards, cross-culture, and multicultural are all popular terms now being used to address the differences and the similarities among groups of people.

Culture can be defined as the totality of social and intellectual information that is transmitted into ways of living by a group of people in order to meet psycho-social and biological needs. It includes beliefs, behavioral patterns, traditions, attitudes, norms, and folkways that are held together to help the group remain functional in society (Terrell, 1995).

Culture is also the additional totality of social and intellectual experiences for an individual, both within their group environment as well as outside the group environment. Everything that a person goes through in their life contributes to their cultural characteristics. Therefore, although members of a group may share some group cultural characteristics, no two individuals can possibly have the exact same individual characteristics. It can be a critical mistake to assume that people of the same cultural group "always" share the same characteristics.

Over the past decades, several researchers have assessed the needs of the African American AIDS client under the realm of cross-cultural counseling or minority issues (Aoki, 1989; Croteau et al., 1993; Fullilove, 1989). "All behavior, including that related to constructive action in the face of HIV and AIDS, occurs within the context of an individual's membership in particular social and cultural groups (Croteau et al., 1993, p. 290)."

The professional and non-professional helper working with the African American client impacted with HIV/AIDS and their families must be knowledgeable and sensitive to the clients' cultural influences and values and how these values have an impact on their clients' behavior. It is essential that the helper be able to "recognize the effects of social oppression directed toward these groups (Croteau, Morgan, Henderson & Nero, 1992, p. 169)."

African Americans currently comprise over 30 million people and approximately 13% of the total population in the United States. They are also the largest minority group in the United States and perhaps one of the most diverse. African Americans can be very traditional as well as non-traditional, representing many religions, levels of income, levels of education, and geographical regions. African Americans also have a wide array of skin tones, hair textures, and facial features. Because of these diversities they can have an equally wide range of personal, behavioral, and social characteristics.

There is, however, one factor almost all African Americans share. That factor is their African and African American history. A history of ancestors who were politically, economically, physically, and emotionally enslaved, robbed of family and community, physically and mentally abused, and considered to be less than human. The subsequent ramifications and struggles to overcome such enslavement include attempting to survive poverty, discrimination, institutional racism, and powerlessness. The many ways African Americans have internalized this history, responded to this history, and reacted to this history are the elements that make-up African American culture as it is today (Terrell, 1995).

The cultural and psychological impact of slavery and post-slavery discriminatory behaviors and attitudes continues to appear today among many African Americans in both positive and negative ways. With respect to HIV, AIDS, and African Americans, the impact is often magnified.

COMMON CULTURAL FACTORS

It is important for anyone who is concerned for the welfare and care of another individual to gain information and understanding of the characteristics found common among that person's group environment and culture. In this case, the characteristics should include those found common among many African Americans. According to Sue and Sue (1990) some of the following factors, if not properly understood by others, can cause communication barriers that lead to misunderstandings between African Americans and non-African Americans:

SENSE OF COMMUNITY OR PEOPLE-HOOD

Due to slavery and subsequent implications such as segregation and discrimination, African Americans have had to live near each other for survival, support, and security. In many cases these African American communities were the only places for African Americans to obtain a level of comfort, safety, and happiness.

Whether forced to live together or living together by choice they began to share their struggles as well as their triumphs. African Americans began to feel a sense of family, belonging and group affiliation. Today, this sense of community transcends into more than a geographical area of homes and businesses. Today, the "hood" is a concept of African American togetherness. Whether it is impoverished or not, these African American communities consist of schools, business, churches, and residential areas that offer the one place where African Americans can feel wanted and understood.

This sense of comfort is part of the reason it is so important for African Americans with HIV/AIDS or other health care issues to have medical and social service facilities developed within their neighborhoods. It is more likely that an African American individual, whose comfort level is higher in an African American neighborhood, will seek medical and mental health attention if the facilities are in the "hood." It is also advantageous and more effective for these facilities to have African American staff members and professionals, if at all possible. If this is not possible, then the staff must at least be culturally sensitive to the issues of this population so they can appropriately and adequately attend to the needs of the African American client and/or patient.

Additionally, for individuals in lower socioeconomic levels, the issue of transportation is also a determinant as to whether an individual will seek services outside of the "hood." Many African Americans in these areas still do not have cars or the money to take a cab or bus to other areas of town. For individuals impacted with HIV/AIDS who may also be experiencing pain or physical discomfort, a bus ride that includes a transfer to a second bus downtown can be a very long and difficult ordeal.

Case Story:

In the early 1990s I worked in a predominately White and gay service agency, as an African American therapist. I was attempting to provide culturally sensitive counseling to the few African American clients who at that time had few other places to access HIV related services. Most of my work was with clients who were either provided transportation by the agency, or who were in a crises situation and desperate for help. I tried to develop African American support groups at the agency, but was unsuccessful in my attempt.

Later, I began to provide the same services in an African American owned and operated clinic in the heart of the African American community. The difference in responses were significant. Individual therapy and group therapy began to have regular and long-term attendance.

Much of the change in attendance was because of the distance or mode of travel, but I also noticed that many of my clients lived in African American neighborhoods in other parts of the city. This told me that for some individuals the deciding factor was location, but for others it was the improved comfort level of being in an African American environment.

SUSPICIOUSNESS AND MISTRUST

Over the decades and perhaps centuries, because of racism and oppression as well as personal experiences of today, many African Americans tend to mistrust Whites.

This mistrust seems to exist among African Americans regardless of gender, level of income or education, and place of residence (Terrell, 1995). Once you have been treated poorly simply because of your race, the emotional scars can be overwhelming.

These feelings of mistrust by African Americans are commonly demonstrated by exhibiting signs of suspiciousness. This suspiciousness can be directed toward many facets in the HIV-related arena including health-care professionals, medications, insurance, and statistical reports.

The methods, motives, sincerity, and qualifications of the mental and medical health-care professional is often questioned because of suspected racism or discrimination. It is not unusual for African American clients to wonder if the professional treatment is equal to that of their White counterpart. Additionally, due to insensitive stigmas and discrimination related to HIV, confidentiality is a primary concern for many who are infected. There is often suspicion the professional can not be trusted with such confidential information.

For many African American clients, when an experience appears to be negative or if a mistake is made by the White professional, the first thought is discrimination or prejudice, even when the cause may be simply human error. More information regarding trust issues with respect to counseling and mental health are covered in Chapter Nine.

The true value and need for prescriptions and medications can also receive unusually suspicious attention. Many African Americans feel they may be "being used" as guinea pigs or they aren't getting the best and current med- ication on the market compared to what the White patients may be receiving. The results of medical tests, including HIV testing, are often held in suspicion for the same rea- sons.

African Americans who have jobs with private insurance are also often suspicious. They are concerned that the insurance companies will either drop their policy and/or inappropriately disclose HIV related information to their employer. The fear of disclosure and discrimination is ever- present. It is not unusual for African Americans to avoid utilizing valuable insurance and other needed benefits because of this fear and mistrust.

The African American community at-large is often suspicious and mistrustful of the HIV/AIDS statistics and related HIV/AIDS data regarding African Americans. This suspicion is primarily because of historical misrepresenta- tion, unfair portrayal in the media, and questionable find- ings in research literature. Because of this history of misin- formation it is not uncommon for African Americans to dis- count and ignore the critical impact of HIV/AIDS data that is often reported.

EXTENDED FAMILY

The family system in the African American commu- nity often extends beyond the parents and their children. African Americans have had to take care of each other's children, regardless of bloodline, for centuries. Often this family system was extended due to financial necessity, but many times it was due to a sense of obligation to take care of "their own." African American families would care for and raise both related and non-related children when their parents were not able or available.

Multi-generational homes are also very common. It is common for grandparents to raise their grandchildren. With high incidence of teenage pregnancy, many mothers, their teenage daughter, and the new baby all live in the same household along with the rest of the mother's family. African American children raised by their grandmothers will often grow up to consider their grandmother as their mother. It is also not unusual for cousins to grow up in the same household. Due to these extended family systems, some households will have many individuals living under one roof.

The family system has also been extended due to the need for belonging, protection, and helping of one another. The bonds of the extended family system can also be developed because of the desire to "keep the family from being separated or spread apart." It is often simply a matter of love and values.

Additionally, the mistrust of others tends to further develop the extended family. Avoidance of social, medical, and government institutions is yet another implication. African American families often find it difficult to allow "others", such as a retirement facility, to care for their elderly. The same is often true for someone who needs long-term mental health or medical care. With respect to someone who is living with HIV/AIDS and is also needing long-term care, it is usually their family members that provide the majority of non-hospital care, rather than a hospice or institutional healthcare facility.

There is also the issue of who takes care of the children of people who have AIDS. The parent may be sick and unable to care for them without assistance, or they may have died. Many families are left with the choice of taking-in a family member's children or letting the "state government" take the children into foster care. Consequently, it is usually the extended family that takes care of these children. Many African Americans consider it to be shameful or irresponsible to have their elders, children, and terminally ill family members institutionalized, or even cared for by "others."

TIME ORIENTATION

African Americans have been stereotyped as people who are not conscientious of time and punctuality. In fact, even African Americans have often accepted the stereotype and made fun of the action when it occurs. This stereotype may have some historical significance for its development.

Again, due to institutional racism and economical oppression, African Americans have had to deal with substandard and/or discriminatory treatment when accessing medical, social, government, and other institutional systems. Part of this treatment was having to wait in long lines for service and having to wait for long periods of time to gain certain professional help. Perhaps, at some point in time the person is expecting that he or she will not be seen at the scheduled time, so therefore is not in any hurry to be on time.

When seeking HIV/AIDS related services and health-care management, an individual may have several weekly appointments to attend. In many cases the choices of these services may be extremely limited. If the facility is over-booked or not punctual, the patient may not feel that their own punctuality is necessary or important.

In many cases the issue of punctuality is not totally within their control. Many African Americans with HIV/AIDS have to rely on public transportation in order to make needed appointments. Some are unable to control their time because of other responsibilities such as inflexible work schedules and child-care dilemmas. Many patients cannot afford to miss three to four hours of work, several times a week, in order to go to the doctor. Still others will either have to bring their children with them or pay for someone to care for them. For some African American parents the above choices are not viable options.

Individuals with HIV/AIDS without private insurance are often forced to use county facilities for adequate HIV/AIDS expertise. In the inner city, as is the case for many African Americans with HIV/AIDS, the county facilities are often overcrowded and understaffed and cannot maintain timely appointments. So the consensus is often "why should I be on time?"

Case Story:
David had been diagnosed with AIDS for several years before he began to have complications which required immediate attention. He said that he had not been going to the doctor because he hated to wait hours at a time for medical attention.

BLACK LANGUAGE / EBONICS

Over the past few years, there has been much discussion regarding an African American language which has been more recently referred to as "Ebonics." This African American language is indeed a cultural characteristic of most but not all African Americans. It is a dialect of Standard English that has evolved from slavery and post-slavery adaptation.

Much of this adaptation was developed due to the continued unequal separation and segregation of African Americans from mainstream American society at large. The variations of this African American language are often influenced by age, socioeconomic level, geographic location, and amount and type of institutional education. According to Terrell (1995):

> The extent to which a person identifies with the culture of the speech community has also been found to influence the use of the dialect (Terrell and Terrell, 1981). Individual speakers can also vary along a continuum of

dialect use, employing code switching dependent upon the communicative context.

Since a significant percentage of African Americans living with HIV/AIDS are from geographical locations that often include lower and middle socioeconomic and educational levels, the likelihood of encountering a distinct African American language is increased. This population may not understand much of the medical and mental health terminology, literature, and concepts that are frequently being used in these areas.

Equally important, the professional may not always have a complete understanding of what the African American client may be saying. They also may not always adequately translate the correct and intended meaning.

The African American client may feel as though these professionals "cannot relate" to their experience due to the language differences. It would not be unusual for the African American person to avoid expressing their true feelings or even avoid expressing all of the facts because of differences in use of the language. This type of communication barrier can cause significant misinterpretations, misdiagnoses, and misunderstandings if not properly handled. The client may experience shame or feelings of inferiority and sometimes anger when communicating their thoughts into words.

It is important for those who do not understand Ebonics to use extreme caution and sensitivity in the interpretation and translation of the African American dialect. The following hints may be helpful:

> 1. Ask for clarification, not only to what the client has said but also to what the client means. Also make sure the client understands what you have said and what you mean. Do not make any assumptions.
>
> 2. Do not attempt to mirror the use of the language or some of the terminology. Your interpretation may be inaccurate.
>
> 3. Respect the client and their usage of the dialect, and do not try to correct or make the individual conform to your use of the English language.

RELATED MENTAL HEALTH THEORIES

Researchers and psychologists have conducted studies for decades in an effort to develop effective theoretical approaches that could be used when helping African Americans. The two concepts that will be discussed include Racial Identity and Locus of Control. These concepts help to determine commonality among African Americans that could be used by the mental health professional in order to better understand the individual, as well as the culture. Racial Identity is a psychological model outlining how the

African American mentality may go through different stages of racial identity development. The five stages to be defined are pre-encounter, encounter, immersion-emersion, internalization, and internalization-commitment. Locus of Control is a psychological concept that researchers suggest, due to historical oppression and discrimination, many African Americans have developed an external locus of control, and thereby do not easily prescribe to the ideology of having the power to help themselves through difficult social, political, and economical times.

RACIAL IDENTITY FOR AFRICAN AMERICANS

Helms (1993) defined racial identity as "a sense of group or collective identity based on one's perception that he or she shares a common racial heritage with a particular group" (p.3). She essentially agreed with the pioneers (Cross, 1971; Jackson, 1975; Thomas, 1971) of Black racial identity models that racial identity for African Americans is a developmental process of transformation from one stage to another. Helms (1987) believed each stage depicts a particular set of characteristics for an individual depending on what is "occurring in his or her psycho-social environment" (p. 242; Blackwell, 1994).

In these racial identity models directed toward only African Americans (Cross, 1971; Jackson, 1975; Thomas, 1971), much of the research indicated there were correlation's between stages of racial identity and how African Americans cope with various issues within American society. However, Helms (1993) states that the Cross (1971, 1978) model has been most often used when conducting research and investigating the counseling process and racial identity. Subsequently, this model has been amended by Helms and some of her colleagues (Carter & Helms, 1987; Helms, 1984, 1987, 1989; Parham & Helms, 1981). The Cross model is described as follows:

The Cross Model

The Cross model (1971) explains the racial identity stages an African American can pass through in search of an African American identity (Cross, 1980; Hall, Cross, & Freedle, 1972). The Cross model is also called "the Negro-to-Black conversion" (Cross, 1971, p. 14).

> Pre-encounter   (The first stage). "In the pre-encounter stage a person is programmed to view and think of the world as being non-Black. The person's world view is dominated by Euro-American determinants" (Cross, 1971, p. 15).
> *Example:* A person who only wants to live in the White community and interact with Whites.

> Encounter (The second stage). "Encounter entails two steps: first, experiencing the encounter; second, beginning to re-interpret the world as a consequence of the encounter: (Cross, 1971, p. 17). In this stage, a shocking event occurs that effects the person's

point of view, helping the individual better understand his or her identity in a new way (Cross, 1980; Hall et at., 1972).

Example: A person is called a racial slur for the first time, or perhaps a person who is discriminated against at work because of his or her race.

Immersion-emersion (The third stage). In this stage the person relates all aspects of their life toward being African American (Cross, 1971, 1980; Hall et al., 1972) and "attempts to purge him or herself of their former world-view and old behavior (Ramseur, 1989, p. 229)."

Example: Someone who is "pro-Black only," wears mostly African garments and is perhaps angry at all Whites.

Internalization (The fourth stage). "This stage signals the resolution of conflict between the 'old' and 'new' world views (Cross, 1980, p. 86)." This person makes these new values his or her own and regards Black as their primary reference group (Ramseur, 1989).

Example: This person may be going to a Black church and may live in a Black neighborhood, but is also fairly functional working with Whites.

Internalization-commitment (The fifth stage). The individual looks for interests and activities to prove or show the new African American identity (Ramseur, 1989), yet is also sensitive to the plights of all oppressed peoples. This person has developed an inner sense of security and now can own and appreciate unique aspects of their culture as well as those in mainstream US culture. The person is not necessarily in conflict with White dominant cultural ways. There is now the belief there are acceptable and unacceptable aspects in all cultures. Cross (1971) sees this fifth stage as being the ideal stage for an African American to be considered psychologically healthy (Ramseur, 1989).

Example: This person may be someone who fights for the rights of African Americans but also the rights of all who are oppressed. He or she is also able to see the good in all races.

These African American developmental stages can be utilized by the professional who desires to help a client move toward a balanced stage of racial identity. If the helper can determine the stage most closely resembling the characteristics of the client, insight into cultural issues can be learned.

Literature suggests that racial identity stages can, but not always, begin with an African American denying himself or herself of an African American identity and then moving toward a more complete and balanced identity. These stages are designed to end in a more secure sense of African American identity with a healthier perspective of how that identity can better fit into the current American society. It may be helpful to the client for the professional to help the client move toward the final stage. The helper must realize the African American individual can, however, come into the counseling process at any one of the stages. Additional research and reading in this area should be conducted, if one chooses to pursue this model of intervention (Blackwell, 1994).

LOCUS OF CONTROL

External control - Rotter (1982) suggested that when an individual believes the events that occur in his or her life are "the result of luck, chance, fate, as under the control of powerful others, or as unpredictable because of the great complexity of the forces surrounding him (p. 171)," that belief is called external control.

Example: One who believes their future is in the hands of the government's political system, or God's will, or perhaps a particular doctor or medical system.

Internal control - However, if the individual perceives the event is based upon his or her own characteristics, it is called internal control (p. 171).

Example: This person may believe their future is guided by perhaps eating right, exercise, getting an education or being more assertive at work.

Rotter called these beliefs an individual's "locus of control" (Achterberg & Lawlis, 1990, p.3). Through the years, researchers have provided explanations of locus of control that have cultural, social and political implications. For example, Lefcourt (1982) stated:

> When one acquaints oneself with the massive literary out-pouring regarding the lives of impoverished peoples, displaced persons, and of members of denigrated minority groups, a common characteristic is that of abject helplessness and a sense of despair. To people who live in continuously adverse circumstances, life does not appear to be subject to control through their own efforts. Only through some outside intervention do events seem to be alterable, and such intervention is a rare occurrence (p. 19).

Phares (1976) believed it is a good assertion that locus of control is "related to differences in access to power or to the presence of social barriers to group mobility" (p. 44). He argued, evidence shows African Americans and other lower socioeconomic groups generally have an external belief system.

Forward and Williams (1970) questioned the relationship of internal-external control concepts and how they apply to minority populations. They believed when such an individual exhibits high externality on the Rotter IE Scale

(Rotter, 1966) it may show "a realistic appraisal of external forces at work in the ghetto rather than the more commonly assumed belief that events are due to fate or chance (p. 78)."

Forward and Williams also suggested high internality may indicate feelings of "worthlessness and self-blame for the negative aspects of his existence rather than a feeling of personal efficacy in its more common positive sense (p.78)." All of these versions of the theory must be considered when working with clients.

Health Attribution Theory

What an individual believes about their past and future has a strong impact on their behavior (Achterberg & Lawlis, 1990, p.3). Heider (1958) concluded, the explanation people have concerning events occurring in their lives has a great deal to do with the shaping of their behaviors. These explanations were labeled attributions (Achterberg & Lawlis, 1990).

Health attribution theory is concerned with an individual's (regardless of race) belief system regarding his or her health (Achterberg & Lawlis, 1990). Research regarding locus of control in settings of a medical nature generally "show people who have an internal locus of control take more active roles in maintaining and regaining health" (Achterberg & Lawless, 1990), p.3.) It should be noted there is limited research conducted specifically on African Americans, locus of control, and health issues.

These theories of locus of control can also be used in the counseling process. If the professional can help move the African American HIV/AIDS clients' belief system of external control towards internal control, especially with respect to health-care, and help the client develop a positive level of racial identity, the quality of life for that individual could be improved significantly.

The objective is to help the individual take a more proactive interest in what the professionals are doing or not doing, as well as a more proactive role in what they can do or not do to help themselves. It is hoped the client will begin to add to the professionals' care by doing such things as eating better, exercising more, taking medications regularly, resting, and reducing stress.

These theoretical concepts can be used as tools for mental health professionals in helping African Americans realize a stronger level of self-identity and self-responsibility. With improved cultural sensitivity and education of the helper; enhanced levels of identity and responsibility of the African American person with HIV/AIDS, substance abuse and sexuality concerns; quality care and quality of life are imminent.

CHAPTER THREE

HIV Diagnosis and Early Intervention

Being infected with HIV/AIDS can lead to many years of physical and emotional problems which can eventually become life threatening (Goodwin, 1992; Mitchell, 1990). Fortunately, because of modern medicine, a person living with HIV/AIDS and who is under proper medical, physical, and mental care is now able to live with the effects of the disease longer and healthier than ever before. Along with early diagnosis, and early intervention many individuals can now utilize medical "treatment that may slow the spread of infection and retard the progression of infection to the more severe forms of the disease (Jenkins et al., 1993, p. 109)."

DELAYED MEDICAL ATTENTION

An individual can be infected with HIV/AIDS for months and even years before they begin to see any visual and/or physical signs of the disease. If a person is not routinely tested they may carry the disease for a long period of time without knowing they have been infected. This is also a long period of time without obtaining proper medical attention.

This period of time, without a diagnosis, can be very dangerous for several reasons. The first reason is, these are the months and perhaps years the infected individual could be receiving effective HIV/AIDS related medical attention that will help keep him or her from experiencing many of the physical problems and illnesses that are often associated with having the disease. It is not unusual for some African Americans to find out their bodies have already been seriously impacted by the virus prior to getting help. Many become sick or experience some medical problem, seek treatment for the ailment with a doctor, and then at the doctors request, get tested for HIV.

DELAYED HIV/AIDS EDUCATION

Second to medical attention is the need for proper education and mental health assistance. It is crucial that individuals impacted by HIV/AIDS get current and effective information about the disease before they are shocked with their first symptoms. Early education gives HIV/AIDS educators time to provide individuals with information that may keep them from developing psychological problems later on. This information can prepare them for some of the physical ailments they may or may not experience. This information may also help them avoid many of the emotional experiences common with people having HIV/AIDS. Such emotional experiences include depression, anger, fear, and denial.

RISK TO OTHERS

Third, this is also a period of time the infected person could unknowingly expose others to infection. Perhaps if the individual knows they have HIV/AIDS, they would be more conscientious of behaviors that put others at risk of becoming infected. If they don't know they are infected, how can they tell others or know to protect others? Furthermore, they could also be putting themselves at additional risk for further infection.

Many African Americans are not aware, due to the many strains of the virus, they can become re-infected by continuing to practice risky behaviors. Along with the previously mentioned HIV/AIDS education, individuals can learn effective ways to avoid putting themselves and others at risk.

IMPACT ON LOVED ONES

A fourth reason for early diagnosis concerns the other people who are involved in the life of the person with HIV/AIDS. These people also need time to adjust. Included in this group are the sexual partners or IV drug-use partners the infected individual may have come in contact with. They should be notified of their need to be tested. This will allow them time to get adequate help for themselves and to further reduce the spread of HIV to others. Another group of people involved with the infected individual and who may need to know of the diagnosis are caring and sensitive family members or loved-ones. These are people who could be instrumental in providing social and moral support for the infected individual. Loved-ones are also often in need of psychological assistance and proper education.

The early days of an HIV diagnosis are critical in the development of a positive and healthy life in the years to come. Unfortunately, due to psychological fears, denial, and ignorance, many African Americans avoid getting tested and therefore do not get the appropriate diagnosis until they start to have health-related problems. It is not unusual for many African Americans to seek medical help and diagnosis only after they began to experience physical symptoms and/or unexplained illnesses. It can be a great shock to face not only a first diagnosis but also first actual physical symptoms all at the same time.

PRE-DIAGNOSIS ISSUES

FEAR OF KNOWING

Many African Americans "just don't want to know." These individuals usually suspect they have been infected but just won't face it. Or they at least know they could have been exposed to the virus. Unfortunately, they choose not to be tested. They may know of someone they were involved with who has the disease, or perhaps they had a friend or lover die with the disease. They somehow feel, as long as they don't get tested, they won't have to deal with it. These individuals can be dangerous to our society. Without a diagnosis they can continue to lie to themselves and others. Subsequently, they are not only complicating their chances for survival, but also complicating the chances of survival for others.

DENIAL

There are also many African Americans who know they have HIV/AIDS, or are at least reasonably sure they have it, but continue to think and behave as though they do not. They don't seek proper medical attention and don't change their health-related behaviors. And if they are active in risky behaviors such as drug usage or sexual promiscuity, they continue to impact the lives of others.

Denial manifests itself in many different ways. Some individuals may say the "test results were wrong" or they believe the professionals "don't know what they are talking about." They may say "I feel too good to have HIV." Without proper education about the disease, it is often difficult to accept the diagnosis, especially when the individual with HIV is feeling and looking in the best of health. They may avoid going to places where they may see people who may have HIV, such as clinics, support groups, or social gatherings. They often avoid people and places that might connect them to HIV/AIDS or might make them "face it."

Case Story:
    Kay was an African American woman who showed no physical signs or known symptoms of HIV. At the request of her boyfriend, she came into the clinic to get tested for HIV. Upon receiving the news her test results were positive, she refused to accept the results as accurate and requested a second test. After receiving the same results, she asked for yet another and then another re-test. All of the results were the same. Still dissatisfied, she said she was going to go to a private doctor and get tested again.

IGNORANCE

    Lack of knowledge is also problematic in the African American community. Many individuals are still not educated with the correct information. Some still believe many of the myths and stereotypes they have seen on TV or have heard from friends. Many are still not aware of the ways one can become infected. Many are not aware of the symptoms that often appear in the early stages of infection. Still others are not aware of the modern medical therapy and intervention that is available. Some individuals still think having AIDS is automatic death.

    These are all subjects that should be discussed with a doctor, nurse, or other HIV/AIDS related professionals. Information from TV, movies, or even from friends is not always accurate, and sometimes it is misleading and dangerous. Even when the client is educated about HIV/AIDS from a professional, hearsay, myths, and stigmatization may still prevail in the mind of the individual.

If this is indeed the client's perspective, it will then require the professional to be both an educator and a counselor. It will be important for the professional to be knowledgeable of HIV/AIDS and to accurately and effectively pass that knowledge on to their client as needed.

POST DIAGNOSIS

Once the individual has accepted the initial diagnosis, he or she must learn how to live and cope with the many HIV/AIDS realities of life. Historically, African Americans have had to psychologically deal with stressors, mentally and physically, of various sorts since the beginning of slavery (Cochran & Mays, 1993; Croteau et al., 1993). Due to racism and oppression, African Americans tend to react to issues (Croteau et al., 1992, 1993; Dalton, 1989) differently than their non-African American counterpart. Living with HIV and AIDS is yet another one of those issues (Dalton, 1989).

> Upon the acceptance of an HIV diagnosis, the early feelings and thoughts that an individual may experience can include shock, anger, fear, depression, confusion, isolation, and even relief. These feelings can co-exist in various combinations at various times, but they can also occur independently.

Case Story:

Dan, a 39-year-old African American gay man had been diagnosed with HIV for four years. All four of those years he had been on a path to self-destruction. He did not care about anyone, including himself. He was angry at the world for his life as a gay Black man, and even more angry that he had HIV. He used and abused drugs on a consistent basis and consequently ended up in prison for several years due to drug-related activity. He had been in several unhealthy relationships, trying to find "someone to make him feel better."

He did not want any help, especially substance abuse recovery and certainly not any medical help that would let anyone know that he had HIV. Eventually, he ended up in the hospital with pneumonia for several weeks. For the first time he thought he was going to die. After his hospital recovery, he was more depressed and angry than ever. He ended up abusing more drugs, and once again in the hospital. After several such episodes of illness, his depression, fear of dying, and physical discomfort overwhelmed him to the point that he finally sought professional help.

Years later, Dan, admitted to me that he was now glad that he had HIV. He said, if it were not for HIV, he knows he would have been dead anyway from drugs and his drug-related behavior. He said the quality of his life, even with HIV, is better than the quality of his life before he had HIV, because for the first time in over 20 years, he was free of drugs, taking care of himself, and trying to do something

*positive to help others. He also said, if it had not been for
HIV "waking him up" he would not have made it.*

Hence, the development of the Holland-Blackwell
Model of HIV/AIDS Counseling Intervention, designed for
African Americans. This model is explained further in the
next few chapters. It is designed as a counseling tool to provide individuals with information and guidance to help
them better understand and appreciate the African American
who is infected and/or impacted by HIV/AIDS.

The counseling goal is to help the client and their
loved-ones become self-empowered to take adequate and
successful care of themselves, and therefore assist in
extending not only the quantity of their life but also the
quality of their life.

ASSESSING EARLY MENTAL HEALTH NEEDS

When a person is initially diagnosed and willing to
obtain professional help, it is a critical time for appropriate
assessments to be made by the helping professional. These
assessments are not only needed for physical and medical
health needs, but also for mental health needs. Once the
person has received the initial diagnosis, it is imperative
these mental health assessments be thorough and culturally
sensitive.

CRISIS INTERVENTION

Because the diagnosis can be a shock to some individuals, there may be a need for the professional to administer crisis intervention skills and techniques. These initial feelings range from suicidal ideation to homicidal ideation. They could also range from severe and destructive anger to severe and destructive depression. Although these are not the most frequent responses, they can indeed occur. Of course, if the person is in evident danger of harming themselves or anyone else, the proper legal and medical authorities must be notified. Fortunately, culturally-sensitive support, education, and information are the most significant intervention tools in fighting most crises.

HIV/AIDS BASIC EDUCATION

When working with an African American client who is infected with the virus, it is first important to gain their trust and confidence. At the same time, it is also important to assess that individual's stage of mental or emotional health. A very large part of assisting the individual with mental health care is providing basic HIV and AIDS education and information. This can first be determined by assessing their current level of education with respect to basic knowledge about the disease, their health, and what is happening to their body.

Gaining trust and assessing HIV/AIDS knowledge with a client, can usually be done at the same time. Educating the client, answering any questions they may have and dispelling any myths, will usually help the client to recognize and appreciate the professional's level of concern and expertise. Correct education and information may also help relieve some stress, anxiety, and depression. Because the information about HIV/AIDS care changes rapidly, it is best not to use booklets or pamphlets that are several years old.

Adequate education and information will help reduce the client's stress level and help improve their comfort level. If handled effectively, it will help to set the stage for later discussions of more personal issues and at the same time it will also help the professional determine the general mental state of the client. It should aid the professional in making the decision to perform only crisis intervention versus counseling and other forms of assistance.

When working with an African American client with HIV/AIDS it is important to understand, from the individual's perspective, they may or may not even know the difference between HIV and AIDS. Therefore, it would be helpful for the professional to first determine from the client how they view their current situation and/or diagnosis.

The professional should assess the individual's knowledge level of his or her HIV/AIDS status. It is also helpful for the professional to inquire about the clients level of prior exposure to the effects of the disease from others. This information will make a significant difference on how formal or informal the professional should use the HIV and AIDS terminology. To many African Americans, HIV and AIDS are one and the same. This clarification of information can be particularly helpful for individuals who are in the early stages of HIV and not yet AIDS-diagnosed.

AIDS is caused by the human immunodeficiency virus (HIV). By killing or impairing cells of the immune system, HIV progressively destroys the body's ability to fight infections and certain cancers. The term AIDS applies to the most advanced stages of HIV infection (NIAID, 1994.)

It is also important for the professional to understand, due to racism, discrimination, and the lower socioeconomic status of many of these clients, there may be insufficient numbers of effective and appropriate HIV/AIDS education and prevention programs culturally designed for the African American community.

NEGATIVE OR FALSE STEREOTYPES AND STIGMAS

The helper needs to know how much of what the client knows is fact or fiction. There is a host of mis-information, old information, negative information, and exaggerated information. This type of information is what helps to develop myths and stereotypes that often take years if not decades to correct. These myths and stereotypes come from various sources, both public and private. The public sources include old news stories, movies, TV shows, magazines, and books. Some of this information may have been accurate at the time it was developed, but now is outdated and no longer helpful information. Some of it is insensitive, judgmental, and potentially destructive.

The private sources include hearsay from family, friends, or associates. Keep in mind, whether public or private, people generally like to talk about what is most interesting, unusual, and even negative rather than what is the truth and perhaps a bit boring. These fictions or "war stories" usually cause the most emotional trauma. It is very dangerous for an individual to assume what happened to one person with HIV/AIDS is also going to happen to the next, especially when it comes to the various physical and mental possibilities. Every person is different and their response to the disease is equally different.

Due to the many forms of inaccurate information about HIV and AIDS, many uninformed African Americans are mainly consumed with thoughts of suffering, losing all of their weight, and dying. Current and effective education and information will help the individual understand, with proper care they can possibly avoid many major AIDS-related health problems.

NEEDS ASSESSMENT

For many African Americans, even when properly educated about HIV/AIDS, it is difficult to even think about HIV/AIDS because they are simply trying to survive. Daily struggles of survival, such as paying rent, getting or keeping a job, or feeding a family, will often take priority over

HIV/AIDS acceptance and maintenance. This concentration on survival may perpetuate the lack of urgency in acquiring adequate care, medication, and education. If this is indeed the situation, it will then require the professional helper to also be a source of information about various services, financial aid, and HIV/AIDS agencies available for client needs.

Another major tool for gaining trust and helping a new client is to help them to get into the appropriate social and service systems designed to help individuals with HIV/AIDS. Employment, financial assistance, housing, food, clothing, transportation, child care, chemical dependency, medical, and legal issues are often the primary concerns of these people, particularly if they are in a fixed, low, or no income level. Fortunately, many of the large urban areas are now developing programs and services, agencies, and clinics that are designed to help individuals with HIV/AIDS. It is going to be difficult to offer any significant emotional counseling until this individual is able to get some of his or her basic survival needs met first.

The culturally-sensitive professional can best prepare these African American clients with the skills they will need to access these various programs and services. The professional may need to help them understand the importance of patience when keeping needed appointments. Long waits at often very busy clinics, hospitals and agencies are common. They need to understand these places may be understaffed or have overworked doctors, nurses, caseworkers, and other professionals.

For many African Americans, because of pride or embarrassment, it may be very difficult for them to "ask" for such help. Therefore it will be helpful for the professional to offer as much as possible, to help open the door for more dialogue. This may help decrease any fear or anxieties about various needs the client may have.

BASIC EDUCATION LEVEL (NON-HIV/AIDS-RELATED)

Much of the African American HIV/AIDS population is concentrated in metropolitan areas. These areas are often areas of poverty, unemployment, discrimination, and drug abuse. Unfortunately, subsequent effects of such a lower socio-economic level of existence also manifests itself in lower levels of education. It is not enough for the professional to gain an assessment for HIV/AIDS related education, but they must also achieve an assessment for the client's level of general education.

Unfortunately, even in today's modern society, we still have African Americans who have minimal education. And with respect to African Americans with HIV/AIDS, a portion of this population has very long substance abuse histories brought on by a host of other emotional and childhood issues. Because of some of these problems they may have dropped out of school at an early age.

This assessment is essential for many reasons. The first reason for such an assessment is HIV/AIDS and the associated medical terminology can be difficult to understand. Along with lower levels of education often come lower levels of self-esteem. Doctors and nurses can sometimes be intimidating to people in lower socio-economic groups. Couple this with the added possibility of cultural insensitivity or discrimination, and the African American client may become confused, disinterested, or simply misunderstand what is expected. And many African Americans may be too proud to admit this.

The second reason for the helping professional to know the general education level of the client is to avoid giving the client literature, pamphlets, or asking them to read or write when it is perhaps inappropriate for their level of education. It can be very embarrassing for a client to admit they can't read or understand, so they most often will not tell the professional about this issue. The propensity to have to learn about the surrounding treatments and services, and the need to understand the multitude of pamphlets, books, and other literature all yield a high need for general education and comprehension.

The third reason for a helping professional to be aware of the client's general level of education is due to the frequent need to read and complete various forms and applications when accessing public and private facilities and service providers. Clients may need assistance in properly completing applications for financial aid or other AIDS related social services.

If the helping professional is aware of the client's limits with respect to formal education and ability to read and write, he or she may be able to help the client in other ways, by assisting them with completing forms, reading and explaining pamphlets to them, or perhaps helping them to get into high school equivalence programs. Along with higher levels of education often comes a higher level of self-esteem, confidence, and self-empowerment.

EARLY COUNSELING INTERVENTION ISSUES

NEED FOR ADDITIONAL COUNSELING AND GUIDANCE

Once the above information is properly assessed, the general direction of therapeutic counseling and guidance can be addressed. The focus and direction of counseling can be determined, and the professional counselor is better able to develop a treatment plan that is sensitive and appropriate to the needs of the client. This treatment plan can be appropriate for both the client as an individual and for the client as a member of his or her larger community or cultural environment.

From a counseling perspective there are numerous issues and concerns significant to many African Americans impacted with HIV/AIDS that may be frequently encountered. In addition, the counselor must also gain an awareness of the client's understanding of the counseling process.

The mental health counseling process is still foreign to many African Americans. Again, due to the myths and stereotypes presented in the media, many African Americans still think "you have to be crazy" to seek counseling. Still others think of counseling in terms of career counseling or school counseling. Jue and Kain (1989) believe the AIDS infected individual who is seeking counseling is often not familiar with the counseling process and may be expecting to receive only social assistance information and "concrete services" rather than discussions of feelings. And yet many African Americans think of counseling as some form of "brain washing" and "manipulation."

Therefore, it may be necessary to first discover the client's view of counseling and, second, to education the client as to what the counseling process is designed to do. Included in the education of the counseling system should be some discussion about client confidentiality, the structure of the counseling process, the type of treatment plan, the goals and expectations of counseling process, and the ethical and legal guidelines.

How the African American client and culture view counseling is an important issue for the counselor to examine. The counselor must be sensitive to "social and familial" roles associated with the client who is infected with AIDS (Jue & Kain, 1989). Research (Croteau et al., 1992) suggests, programs which incorporate such issues deserve more consideration among professionals who work with HIV/AIDS multicultural groups.

It is imperative the counselor have an understanding of what emotional support means to the client. The African American client who is diagnosed with HIV/ AIDS may see counseling as an alternative way to decrease the burden on friends and family, or they may see discussing such issues with a stranger entirely too personal (Jue & Kain, 1989). Many African Americans still prescribe to the old saying "you keep family business in the family." Due to the complex issues of African Americans with HIV/AIDS who may also be hiding sexuality or substance abuse from their families, counseling may be the only viable option.

While the professional has been helping the African American client gain a better understanding of the disease and making them aware of the various forms of support services, the client is hopefully beginning to not only reduce their level of distress and anxiety about their diagnosis, but also gain some level of trust and comfort with the professional and the helping process. Also, while the African American client impacted with HIV/AIDS is adjusting to a new physical life, it is now appropriate for the professional to also begin helping the individual with a new emotional life. Due to modern medicine and technology, a person with HIV/AIDS can successfully live with the ups and downs of their physical and emotional health for many years and avoid becoming primarily consumed with death and suffering.

ACCEPTANCE OF DIAGNOSIS

After the HIV/AIDS diagnosis, one of the most common issues that seems to come forth in the early counseling sessions is dealing with the individual's level of acceptance which can come in many forms, including post-HIV/AIDS testing, post-denial, and post-first symptom.

Acceptance of the diagnosis is paramount to helping the individual through a smoother transition into medical and mental health treatment.

POST-DENIAL

For those who have been in denial for a long time, this issue of acceptance can be traumatic because they have found out their diagnosis is indeed real and they have perhaps gone years without adequate medical and mental health attention. These thoughts often lead to feelings of anger and guilt. The anger is often directed at themselves for having gone so long without medical attention and allowing the effects of HIV/AIDS to worsen. There may also be anger at self for continuing risky or unhealthy behaviors and therefore exacerbating the problem. The thoughts of acceptance after a long period of denial may also lead to increased feelings of guilt. Some of the guilt is due to the related feelings of not facing the reality sooner and perhaps spreading the infection to others because of risky behaviors.

POST-HIV TESTING

The time period immediately after testing for HIV, is also an emotional time. The individual has usually built up stress and anxiety worrying about the results. They have probably tried to prepare themselves for the worst but realize it is still difficult. Anxiety and depression are often the feelings that begin to occur because the person has been thinking about it so much. They are anxious to find out but are still fearful of the results. These clients have had little time to adjust to the news.

Many African Americans do not consider themselves in high-risk-of-infection categories. Hence, they are often "in shock" because they did not suspect the test results to be positive. After the initial shock, periods of anger may develop toward the person they feel may have exposed them to the disease. Later they often become severely depressed because they wonder "why," especially if they felt they were in a low-risk category.

Those African Americans who knew they were in a high-risk category have somewhat different feelings. There is still the shock and anger, but there is sometimes a feeling of relief in at least knowing the truth so they can stop wondering.

POST-FIRST SYMPTOM

There are African Americans who don't accept the realities of an HIV/AIDS diagnosis until they have their first visual signs or symptoms. This is often thought to be a harsh awakening. This population of people was still "hoping" the diagnosis was not true, or that maybe they would be "one of the lucky ones who doesn't have symptoms." And for some, it provides the individual with fears of more illness and perhaps death. There is usually a sense of panic and eventually more depression, at least until the symptoms go away.

When the level of acceptance begins to occur, many of these African Americans find it difficult to cope.

They are finally ready to talk about their feelings, thoughts, and behaviors. And they are getting months and perhaps years worth of emotions out for the first time. Along with acceptance of the diagnosis also comes acceptance of a host of interrelated issues, such as the behaviors that caused them to contract the disease in the first place, how their diagnosis is going to impact others, and the quality and quantity of their future.

There are issues that the helping professional can discuss with the client that may help with their level of acceptance:

> 1. Discussion about the importance of early and regular physical, mental, and in some cases spiritual help. Help them to realize that effective maintenance is the key to survival. Help them to see the advantages of seeking help now rather than later.

> 2. Discussions of how HIV/AIDS affects everyone differently and to not get overwhelmed by what they have seen or heard from others. Much of this information is often the negative aspects of HIV/AIDS. There are many positive outcomes individuals may not have heard about. Also, every person's body is different, their reaction to disease and medication is different, and they all take care of themselves differently.

3. Discussions on the great advances of HIV/AIDS medical treatments, research, technology and services. It is important individuals know that HIV/AIDS disease five years ago is much different than HIV/AIDS today. There is more hope and improved quality and quantity of life since the onset of HIV/AIDS in the African American community. Some individuals may still be thinking in terms of the way HIV/AIDS started out in the gay White community.

4. Discussion on how it is "okay to ask for help." An HIV/AIDS diagnosis can be overwhelming. Many feel it may be too much to deal with. It is important they realize that they don't have to deal with it alone. There are professionals, volunteers, support groups, and a host of other forms of help that can lighten the burden.

DISCLOSURE

When an individual has come to some level of acceptance of their own HIV/AIDS status, it is only the beginning of dealing with yet another issue. This is the issue of disclosure. Disclosure issues can be very complicated, stressful, and emotional. With many African Americans disclosure is the most difficult of all of the issues, because for some it is not only disclosing the well-kept secret of having a terminal illness, but it could also be disclosing the extremely well-kept secret of one's sexuality, sexual behaviors, or chemical addiction.

As mentioned earlier, African Americans are well trained not to talk about their personal business. But with an HIV/AIDS diagnosis, subsequent illness, medication, and frequent doctor visits, it is difficult to keep this completely confidential. Many African Americans experience multiple levels of shame. They are ashamed of what impact their infection might have on their families, friends, church, and co-workers. They are especially fearful of the impact their infection might have on children and parents.

In most cases, these people want to tell their loved ones, but just don't know how or just can't work up the courage. Many are fearful of being rejected, discriminated against, or hurting someone else. The following are some skills that may be helpful when working with disclosure to family and friends:

1. It is best to disclose to only those individuals the client feels have a need to know.
2. It is best to disclose to those individuals the client can trust.
3. It is helpful for the professional to facilitate the disclosure if the client can't seem to do it alone.
4. The client should try to discuss the various issues surrounding the fear with a professional, prior to the disclosure.

Disclosure often becomes an even more serious issue if it is needed to ensure someone who has been exposed to the virus gets tested. Many African Americans find it difficult to inform their sexual partners or needle-sharing partners that they have the virus because they are fearful of being physically harmed or ostracized. This can be a very critical issue because the quality of someone else's life is now at stake.

The helping professional should encourage the client to do what they can to notify those individuals that they may have exposed to the virus so they can be tested. If this seems too difficult or dangerous for the client to do, then the professional should inquire with various HIV/AIDS resources about Anonymous Report Programs. Some areas have such programs that are usually very effective. In anonymous reporting programs, the person who is being notified is only told that they "may need to be tested," but are not told who made the report.

Part II:

The Holland-Blackwell Model

Of HIV/AIDS Counseling Intervention

The Holland-Blackwell Model

From a helper's point of view, there are numerous issues and perspectives significant to many African American HIV/AIDS clients that may be frequently encountered. It is incumbent upon the effective counselor to not only become fully aware of these issues and perspectives, but also to become knowledgeable of the therapeutic value in respecting, appreciating, and properly addressing these issues.

As mentioned earlier, African Americans fall into several high-risk-of-infection behavior categories. These categories primarily include homosexual/bisexual males with and without histories of intravenous drug abuse, heterosexual intravenous drug abusers, and heterosexual contacts of persons with HIV/AIDS or at increased risk for HIV/AIDS.

When HIV/AIDS was thought to be predominantly a "gay, White, male disease", the risky behaviors were somewhat known and limited to a few exposure categories. Therefore, the focus of counseling and prevention could be more specific. Once the risky behavior was addressed, the primary counseling concerns were to help the individuals live with the issue of HIV/AIDS as successfully as possible. These gay White males who were already infected had no forewarning and did not know about HIV/AIDS. Therefore the concentration on "how they got HIV" was very important. It was most needed for education and prevention, so that spreading of the disease could be avoided.

For the African American community, the exposure categories are much more complex. How one got infected is not limited to only a few behaviors. The issue of how one got infected is also not limited to inadequate education and prevention. Although it may seem to be unnecessary to concentrate on the past and take the position of "what's done is done," with the African American client it is paramount for the helper to be able to get a complete picture of the person's history. The helper needs to get a clear picture and continue working with that picture throughout the counseling relationship.

The majority of the African American HIV/AIDS impacted clients come from one or more of four basic psycho-social paths. It is usually from one or more of these paths that the counselor must be able to identity, properly choose, and focus-on in order to effectively help the African American client who is impacted by HIV/AIDS. The psycho-social paths include: Substance abuse, Homosexuality and/or Bisexuality, Heterosexuality, and Caregiver. It is very important the helper is able to identify, understand, and/or at least respect the "world-view and reality" of that client when he or she enters the helping relationship.

Chapters Four through Seven outline the Holland-Blackwell Model of HIV/AIDS Counseling Intervention with respect to these psycho-social issues. It holds the basic philosophy that "behind every behavior is a feeling". Whether the feelings and behaviors are positive or negative, the premise still holds true. For the purpose of this book, the behaviors in question include substance abuse, at-risk sexual behaviors, relational behaviors, other self-destructive behaviors and inappropriate care-giving.

The individual must first be able to identify and address the feelings that led to the behavior. Then they must successfully work through these feelings and learn effective skills and alternative ways to handle these feelings. If done effectively, the individual will be better able to appropriately change the negative behaviors into positive ones. Many of the feelings of African Americans, be they historically based or not, are often very different than that of their non-African American counterpart. Complicated with HIV/AIDS, these feelings can be magnified.

Chapters Eight and Nine outline the Holland-Blackwell Model of HIV/AIDS Counseling Intervention with respect to the four external systems that are frequently encountered for many African Americans. These external systems include the medical, economic, political and counseling systems.

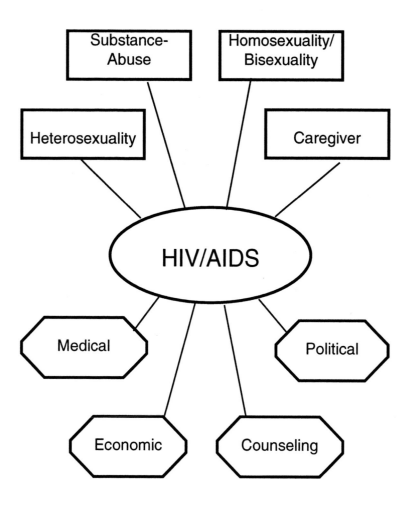

The Holland-Blackwell Model
For African Americans & HIV/AIDS

CHAPTER FOUR

HIV/AIDS and Substance Abuse

According to the Center of Disease Control, of the total African American adult/adolescent AIDS cases reported through June 1999, approximately 37% reported being infected from intravenous drug use (IDU). When studying HIV/AIDS and substance abuse among African Americans, there are two major areas of consideration: active drug and/or alcohol users and those who are trying not to use drug and/or alcohol again. The dynamics of these two groups can overlap from time to time, especially if the client is having multiple relapse episodes.

ACTIVE USERS

It is important to understand it is usually the poorer and less educated drug abuser that will probably share a needle rather than buy new, unused needles (Jue & Kain, 1989). Needle-sharing tends to remain within specific groups. African Americans usually share needles with other African Americans. Often these groups have "ties of friendship and family relationships that bond the group"

(Fullilove, 1989). These ties not only increase the likelihood of multiple addiction but also multiple HIV/AIDS infection within a small group of people. It also increases the spread of the disease within a small community or within a family and, subsequently, within the African American population.

CLEAN VS. RECOVERY

Many African Americans who are actively using drugs and/or alcohol but seeking recovery help do not know the difference between "being clean" and "being in recovery." It is important they understand the difference. In order for African Americans to maintain improved mental health and an increased quality of life they should strive to be successful with both being clean and being in recovery.

The concept of "clean" is basically considered to be physical. If an individual has no alcohol or drugs in their body for a certain amount of time, then they are considered to be clean. Some individuals are able to stop using on their own, but most need professional assistance. If their bodies still crave drugs and if their mind still wants drugs, it is going to be difficult for them to resist. It is important for them to know, as long as they are thinking and behaving like an addict or an abuser, then they are likely to relapse sooner or later.

The concept of "recovery" is basically considered to be mental. If an individual learns how to deal with feelings in a positive way, think in a healthy and productive way, and therefore look at life in a healthier way, they are very likely to be better able to resist relapse. Although some individuals are able to gain and maintain recovery on their own or with the help of friends or family, most individuals may need some type of professional help. Recovery programs are most easily accessible through various in-patient and out-patient facilities.

For many African Americans, because of lack of insurance or financial resources, local 12-step programs such as Alcoholics Anonymous or Narcotics Anonymous are the only viable options. It is important to note, however, there are various AIDS-related agencies that receive funding to help finance both in-patient and out-patient recovery programs for individuals with HIV/AIDS diagnoses.

Because of the mental and physical complexities of substance abuse along with HIV/AIDS, African Americans who are battling both of these issues at the same time will need to become and remain both clean and in recovery for the rest of their lives.

The professional helper must assist the client in understanding that no recovery program is going to work unless the client is sincerely willing and ready to follow the program to the best of their ability and truly try to change their old behaviors. Unless the helper is an experienced and preferably licensed professional, they may need to refer the client to a substance abuse treatment facility or a substance abuse recovery program.

The client must get "clean and sober" in order for any helping professional to be effective with the recovery process. Substance abuse and HIV/AIDS do not mix well for several reasons:

1. Until the helper can get the client "clean" they are not working with the underlying feelings of the individual. The helper is working with the medicated feelings, the covered up feelings, and the self-destructive feelings. It is the underlying feelings that must be dealt with through counseling, in order to effectively help the individual.

2. Alcohol and drugs weaken the physical body and compromise an already compromised immune system, which can further complicate physical problems.

3. Physically, alcohol and drugs do not agree with many of the medications prescribed for HIV/AIDS patients and may cause additional medical problems with some of the body's organs and/or functions.

4. Use and abuse of alcohol and drugs also changes the thinking and decision-making processes, thereby allowing room for an individual to make poor judgments, have a decreased sense of self-control and inhibitions, which in turn increases the chances of complications. One of the complications includes participating in additional "unsafe behaviors." These unsafe behaviors can lead

to getting re-infected with different   strains of HIV, as well as infecting others. Another complication of using poor judgment is being non-compliant in properly taking medication or following doctors instructors. Non-compliance can adversely effect the results of the medical treatment.

If the African American HIV/AIDS client is actively abusing a chemical substance, the helper must work with the client towards "getting them clean" as well as keeping them clean. This can only happen by changing many of their behaviors.   Although IDU is a primary cause of HIV/AIDS infections, it is not the only drug-related behavior that has to be addressed.

Helpers should keep in mind, non-intravenous drugs and alcohol also lead to impaired thinking and rash decisions.   Therefore,   non-intravenous drugs and alcohol, although indirectly, also contribute to the African American HIV/AIDS epidemic.   Consequently, all substance abuse can lead to some of the behaviors that cause not only the spread of the HIV/AIDS infection but also the many post-infection complications.

Because of historical and current ramifications of racism, such as poverty, unemployment and discrimination, alcohol and drug abuse seem to be a continuing source for "coping" within the African American community. With respect to counseling an African American with HIV/AIDS who also has an alcohol and/or drug addiction, the issues are often two-fold. These African Americans may find themselves struggling with both issues concurrently.

MULTIPLE RELAPSES

It is important the helper is prepared to work with both the client's chemical addiction issues and the emotional impact of being infected with the virus. The helper must also be prepared to work with both of these issues for perhaps several years. It is not uncommon for the African American client to become caught-up in a vicious cycle of battling drug addiction in an effort to improve their health, and then, once they are clean, to have to deal with life issues including HIV/AIDS, but this time without drugs and/or alcohol. Multiple relapses are not uncommon, and will therefore require patience, knowledge, and hard work for the helping professional.

CLEAN PAIN

For many African Americans, alcohol and/or drug abuse have become a long-term part of their life. The helping professional must be willing to work with these many long-term issues. It is important the historical, social and political implications also not be overlooked. The subsequent impact of these implications on the feelings and thoughts of African Americans have often led to much hopelessness and depression. These feelings of hopelessness and depression have often led to the behaviors of substance use and abuse.

In treating the African American substance abuser, it may be necessary to explore the possible political and/or social reasons for the client's drug usage. Consequently, it is important for the professional to recognize and respect the client's reality and reason for usage, especially when they speak of his or her substance abuse being an "escape from racism, poverty and discrimination, a substitute for loneliness, divorce, or family separation, or escape from anger or depression." The helper must be sensitive to the African American individual's world view. The helper should attempt to help that person deal with these feelings rationally, rather than choose to avoid the feelings through drugs and/or alcohol.

Once this person is no longer using alcohol and/or drugs to deal with this emotional pain, it may be the first time in many years they begin to experience "clean pain." Clean pain is all of the emotional pain they have been covering up and are now having to learn how to face. Clean pain can be overwhelming, and extremely difficult to face. If it becomes too overwhelming it can lead to a relapse. It may take long-term counseling to help some individuals learn how to cope with this clean pain in new and effective ways. The individual must understand that emotional pain is a part of life, it comes and it goes, hence they have got to embrace it, work with it, and live through it, in order to avoid relapse, and in order to improve the quality of their life. This quality of life includes living with HIV/AIDS.

A typical HIV/AIDS multiple relapse cycle:

1. Work with the feelings that cause the addiction, or resulted from the addiction.

2.Become clean.

3.Experience feelings without alcohol and/or drugs, called "clean pain," and face HIV issues.

4. Possible relapse.

If relapse:

1. Work with the above feelings again along with feelings of relapse.

2. Become clean again.

3. Experience "clean pain" again, including HIV issues again.

4. Possible relapse.

If relapse:

1. Work with feelings again.

2. Work with the feelings of addiction, HIV, and multiple relapse.

3. Become clean again.

4. Experience "clean pain" again, including HIV and relapse issue again.

If **no** relapse.

1. Experience "clean pain" and face HIV issues.

2. No relapse.

FAMILY HISTORY

Historical issues impact African Americans in many ways. One of the most significant ways is through the family. It may be necessary for the helping professional to gain an understanding of the African American individual's family history. Substance abuse issues in many African American families repeat with each generation. It is important for the professional helper to gain an understanding of the family patterns, and related substance abuse behaviors. It is also important to gain an understanding of how these patterns and behaviors impacted the client as a child, as well as an adult. Unfortunately, when addictive behaviors run in families, it is not unusual for other destructive behaviors, including physical and emotional abuse and unhealthy relationships, to also occur.

As a helping professional it is usually helpful to assist the client in seeing and understanding some of this family history, the behaviors, and the patterns. It sometimes helps the individual to gain an understanding of why they may be doing some of the things they do. When an individual can see "some method to the madness," it can be a very insightful and helpful process. Family "trees," or genograms are very helpful in providing the individual with a visual picture of the family and the environment a person may have come from.

Understanding the impact of family behaviors and family patterns is very helpful in reducing individual guilt, gaining a better understanding and providing some hope in an individuals ability to avoid continuing these patterns.

Many African Americans become determined to "break the cycle" of negative family patterns.

MULTIPLE GRIEF AND THE CLIENT

The consequence of multiple addiction and multiple infection can lead to the third issue of multiple deaths. Hence, from a counseling perspective it is not uncommon for this population to also suffer from severe grief issues. Needle sharing tends to remain within specific groups, and among African Americans it is often between family and friends. Needle-sharing not only increases the likelihood of multiple HIV/AIDS infected individuals within a small community or within a family but also increases the likelihood of multiple deaths within that same group. These deaths can be drug related and/or HIV/AIDS related.

The grief issues can be from two separate sources. Some African Americans are grieving the loss of many friends and family due to all causes, including drugs and/or AIDS, which is called multiple grief. Others are perhaps grieving their own potential deaths, which is called anticipatory grief, because they fear the same thing will happen to them. From a counseling perspective it is not uncommon for a client to be suffering from multiple grief and anticipatory grief issues.

Apprehensions and fears from having seen friends and/or family members struggle or suffer with HIV/AIDS, with or without substance abuse, can be devastating and psychologically destructive. The helper must be able to work with the client on these issues so they are better able to look at these issues objectively and individually. The client needs to know the following points of information:

1. HIV/AIDS, even with a history of substance abuse, affects everyone differently and what happened to one person may not happen to another.

2. It is also helpful for them to understand one of the things that makes a big difference in how one survives with HIV or AIDS is how well they take care of themselves medically, emotionally, and spiritually. This care includes getting their bodies free of chemical addiction.

3. Great advances have been made in medical and physical care so some of the problems once common with HIV/AIDS diagnosed individuals a few years ago are now better managed.

4. Caution your African American client against listening to everyone and everything they hear in the streets or from non-professionals about HIV/AIDS. They may be providing erroneous information, old information, or inappropriate personal opinions.

CHAPTER FIVE
Homosexuality and Bisexuality

Traditionally, the African American community has shown great resistance to accepting the issue of homosexuality as a reality in their community and especially within their families. Consequently, this resistance has instilled reluctance, and in some cases discrimination within the African American community in providing community based services, sensitivity, and support for African American homosexuals. For the most part, the various issues and concerns for gay African Americans have been "ignored, made fun of, or something thought to be shameful of."

Homophobia is often internalized in the African American community and has therefore perpetuated the avoidance and ignorance of homosexuality issues. It is because of these "well kept secrets" that many African American homosexual men and women continue to live partly heterosexual lives and are unknowingly increasing the risk of HIV infection to themselves and to others (Dalton, 1989). Approximately 28.5% of the African

American adult/adolescent reported AIDS cases are from those who participated in sex with either a homosexual or bisexual partner (CDC, 1999). Jenkins et al., (1993) state:

> Conservative sexual attitudes may contribute to the increased number of AIDS cases associated with bisexuality by promoting closet behaviors. Because most African Americans are taught that homosexuality is not indigenous to the Black community, many who are homosexual are pressured to maintain heterosexual relationships and those who are bisexual must keep the homosexual relationships discrete (pp. 117-118).

Jue and Kain (1989) believe bisexuality in the minority community is often considered a viable alternative to homosexuality. They found many minority clients express feelings of isolation. Some AIDS infected clients experience "feelings of self-hatred" coupled with "increased separation and alienation from society (Aoki, 1989, p. 31)." Jue & Kain (1989) also state:

> This lack of a large and viable gay minority community with which to identify and the difficulty minority men have in assuming a personal gay or bisexual identity result in a situation of severe isolation—not only from AIDS care but also from AIDS education. Whereas many White gay men receive AIDS

education and information through gay newspapers, gay bars, and gay organizations, this information will not be available to most ethnic minority gay men (p. 139).

Some of the most common issues faced by many African Americans who are diagnosed with HIV/AIDS include facing the realization of their sexuality and, for some, dealing with the issues of "coming out of the closet." Because one of the major exposure categories for contracting HIV/AIDS is related to sexual behaviors and practices, it is often difficult for individuals to adequately address HIV/AIDS without also addressing their sexuality, sexual preferences and sexual behavior.   For many African American gays, it is only because of HIV/AIDS that they are also dealing with their sexuality, with respect to their families and to the African American community at large.

African Americans with HIV/AIDS, who are also gay may find the conflict of dealing with their families and communities with respect to these issues is extremely stressful and emotional. Homosexual African Americans who have HIV/AIDS are often devastated with the prospect of having to face their families with both of the issues, HIV/AIDS and their sexuality. In fact, many clients have a bigger fear of disclosing their sexuality to their families than they do of disclosing their diagnosis. For many African Americans, the reaction to homosexuality ranges from fear and repulsion to rejection and hostility (Fullilove, 1989).

Because of these fears, many homosexual/bisexual African Americans remain secretive and alone without family support rather than face possible rejection from their families and community. It is because of the risk of rejection that many African Americans remain "in the closet" with respect to both their sexuality and their diagnosis, rather than deal with possible rejection, anger, isolation, and discrimination.

Additionally, due to shame and stigmatization of "alternative sexual preference" in the African American community, many African Americans choose to lead "two lives," one that is heterosexual with perhaps a spouse and children and one that is homosexual with perhaps a same sex lover he or she has within the confines of a secret relationship. This "double life" can be extremely stressful and complicated for all parties involved and particularly complicated and dangerous with respect to the prevention and spread of HIV/AIDS.

For the individual who is infected with HIV/AIDS, the guilt and pain due to the possibility of spreading the virus, can be overwhelming. It is not uncommon for the heterosexual partners to be completely unaware their partner is bisexual, only to find out when the infected individual becomes ill or when the heterosexual partner is also diagnosed as having HIV/AIDS.

When working with the homosexual/bisexual African American client that is infected with HIV/AIDS there are several issues that an effective counselor must be aware of. These issues include understanding the varying definitions and meanings of labels and terminology relating to individuals who are homosexual, the African American lesbian, the African American family and associated shame, and the African American church.

DEFINITIONS

The counselor should first get an adequate understanding of what "being homosexual" or "being gay" means to that individual. The terms "gay," "homosexual," "bisexual," and "straight" often have different meanings to different African Americans. One of the major differences in the way African Americans and Whites seem to differ in how they view "gay" is that many White gays think of gay or homosexuality as part of their lifestyle which includes having a preference for a partner of the same sex, whereas many African Americans seem to think of "gay" as mainly sexual behavior.

It is not uncommon for an African American man who has sex with women most of the time and sex with men only during certain situations, to consider themselves as "straight" or heterosexual. These situations most often include men who have had homosexual behaviors only in prison or men who have had homosexual behaviors when influenced by alcohol and drug addiction.

It is also not uncommon for an African American man who has sex with men only as the penetrator to consider himself as straight and his partner who receives the penetration as gay. Some African American men consider only the men who "act feminine" or who have feminine characteristics to be gay. Indeed it is not uncommon for the "masculine-acting" homosexual male to reject or despise the "feminine-acting" homosexual male. Some African American clients prefer not to be referenced as any of the above mentioned labels.

If an African American man has been married or has children as well as a secret homosexual life, he may be even less likely to consider himself as being "gay." He often feels his primary way of life supersedes any secondary interest.

Therefore, it is important for the helper to gain an appreciation for, and respect for that individual's perceptions, beliefs, and definitions. If a helper's assumptions are offensive or insulting, the client-counselor relationship is in jeopardy. Regardless of the name, label, or definition, the counselor must be aware of the possible differences and be able to adjust to the possible implications. The helper must be willing to work with that individual's choice of identity, unless the client is able to and willing to make any changes.

LESBIANS

Lesbian-to-lesbian transmission of HIV/AIDS is not one of the most common exposure categories; however, the presence of lesbians within the African American community as well as within the HIV/AIDS community must still be addressed. Lesbians, as well as others, can still contract the virus through bodily fluid transmission behaviors. Such behaviors include mainly transmission by needle or certain sexual behaviors.

One of the reasons African American lesbians are often present in the HIV/AIDS community is simply due to sensitivity and interest towards the issues and concerns of all gays. Many lesbians have close friendships with gay men who have HIV/AIDS, and unfortunately, due to these friendships, they may have lost many friends through death from AIDS.

The African American lesbian has historically been "invisible" to the African American community. Like the African American homosexual man, the African American lesbian is usually ignored, talked about, or kept "a secret" by the individuals, their families, or by the African American community at large. The African American culture has traditionally held the woman, particularly the "mother," in such high esteem that it is considerably difficult for the community to face and accept lesbian issues.

There seems to be great "shame" within the African American community with respect to lesbians. Many African American bisexual or lesbian women also have children. It is often difficult for her to admit to her children any issues about her sexuality. The professional counselor should be willing to help her face and work through these various issues as well.

In dealing with that shame, the African American lesbian is often secretive and isolated within her own circle. It is here the counselor must be careful to develop appropriate trust levels with the client, in order to establish an effective relationship.

The support system for the African American lesbian may be considerably small, therefore the counselor can be very useful and helpful, especially when he or she is needed to assist the lesbian client in dealing with family, sexuality, relationships, and possible grief issues of AIDS related death. Consequently, the counselor must not only be sensitive and genuine, but also accepting, non-judgmental, and knowledgeable of the world-view of that individual.

The counselor must be aware of the multiple discrimination and multiple rejection issues that might be important to the client. The counselor must be mindful that this possible discrimination and rejection may come from outside, as well as inside of the African American community and family.

FAMILY

With the homosexual African American client diagnosed with HIV/AIDS, there are often intense feelings of shame and guilt, resulting from feelings of having "let the family down" or "embarrassing the family." Homophobia seems to be the prevailing component that prevents sensitivity to homosexuality within the family unit.

Gay and lesbian issues are not widely accepted and are not often taken seriously by a great number of people. Therefore, the counselor who is working with a homosexual/bisexual African American diagnosed with HIV/AIDS is going to have to be able to work with not only sexuality issues but more importantly African American homophobia issues, all within the realm of HIV/AIDS.

This shame issue can be intense from two perspectives. The client may feel shameful of not only their own lifestyle, but may also feel shameful of the impact their lifestyle has had on their family and church.

It is common for the client to be fearful of what "others" are going to say or think about his or her family, or how embarrassed his or her family may be. It is also common for the African American parent to exhibit feelings of responsibility and self-blame for how their child may have "become" gay. Mothers often feel it is something "they did wrong when they were raising the child." Many mothers wonder if perhaps they made their son do traditionally female chores too much, such as washing clothes or caring for younger children.

On the other hand, fathers often exhibit feelings of anger and are often rebellious in thinking that "they did not make a gay boy." Some fathers have been know to disown or even attempt to "toughen-up" their sons as children to "make them change."

These family feelings are very common and often harmful to the family unit. The counselor may have to attempt family counseling to help the members gain a healthy understanding and appreciation for what may be going on with their adult child and homosexuality. Help may also be needed to develop sensitivity and support toward their adult child's diagnosis and sexuality.

CHURCH

The church in the African American community has historically been a powerful and influential force for centuries, serving as a place of comfort, escape, and support. The church is where oppressed African Americans have gone to cope and survive the ramifications of slavery and racism. The traditions and beliefs of the various religions have been intensely passed-on from generation to generation. Church and spirituality are extremely important to many African Americans, particularly in times of crisis, fear, or feelings of hopelessness.

Consequently, the often conflicting feelings of homosexuality, substance abuse, and terminal illness may be overwhelming enough for an individual to seek the confines of the church. Unfortunately, the stereotypes, discrimination, myths, and taboos in regard to these issues and the church, have also been passed on from generation to generation.

The traditional African American church has not been supportive of homosexuality and often solicits condemnation. Some churches and members may reject not only the lifestyle of homosexuality but also the homosexual members. Hence, the one place an African American may want to go, in order to seek help and support may not meet his or her expectations because of prejudice toward both homosexuality and HIV/AIDS. Often the African American gay client is feeling confused and in emotional conflict because of the lack of support they may be receiving from some churches that ironically claim "love for all children of God."

The counselor has to talk to the client and find out their level of spirituality versus religion. It is necessary to know how much of the client's life evolves around their spiritual beliefs and spiritual lifestyle. It is also important to know how much the client relies on their God, the congregation, the minister, the traditional bible, as well as their belief system. The counselor needs to know, at "what level" spirituality and/or religion plays in their individual daily lives, in their lives as a part of the African American community, and, if they are gay, what part it plays in their lives as a homosexual.

For the counselor that is working with the homosexual African American who comes from a strong religious background, the possible pain and fear of rejection from their church, their family, and perhaps even from their belief system in God, may be important issues to deal with. It is important for the counselor to acknowledge that this "need to be accepted by God" is extremely important to this individual and therefore it is necessary for the counselor to help find alternative ways of getting these needs met.

1. The counselor may find it helpful to educate the client about the difference between religion and spirituality. It may be encouraging for the client to gain an understanding that perhaps the physical building and structure of a tangible church is not really the only way to feel the power of one's God. Another alternative may be to explore the possibility that the client may need to perhaps find another church that may be more sensitive to their needs and issues. The African American client needs to know their feelings of faith are still valid wherever they are.

2. In cities, usually larger and more progressive, there are a few churches that are begin-

ning to have AIDS ministries and are more sensitive to AIDS issues. It can be important for the counselor to learn of any such churches for proper client referral. Care must be taken, however. Some of these ministries are designed to only help individuals who are suffering with AIDS from outside of the church and may not necessarily be designed to embrace members of the church who have HIV/AIDS, particularly if the individual is gay.

3. If a client chooses to remain "in secret" then they need to understand the pain and stress often associated with being "in the closet" with their homosexuality. This is a time when a spiritual individual needs the love and support of other spiritual people.

COUNSELING IMPLICATIONS

Because of the depth at which HIV/AIDS is intertwined with the lives of the African Americans who are also homosexual, it is virtually impossible to work with such an individual without addressing both their sexuality and HIV/AIDS concerns. The counselor must be able to deal with both issues simultaneously at times and separately at other times. It is important for the counselor to understand that the stigmatization of HIV/AIDS and homosexuality is so pervasive and rejecting that it may be difficult for the client to face such issues with their family and friends and, therefore, they may have a very limited support system. It is not uncommon for such an individual to continually bounce back and forth between the two issues before finally coming to terms with one or the other. It may be easier for the client to deal with the advent of death and dying rather than deal with disclosing their sexual preference and being infected with HIV/AIDS.

The counselor must be aware of the following implications:

1. If the client is having sexual identity issues, then it is a good possibility that he has infected others, but has not been able to tell them. The counselor needs to help with disclosure so others who may be infected can get tested and, if need be, receive early intervention. This is also needed to help avoid further spread of the virus.

2. If the client is having identity issues, then it is best to help that individual gain some sense of comfort or acceptance of themselves before they are able to face and discuss this with others.

3. To the client, being African American, gay, and diagnosed with HIV/AIDS, is often considered as being a triple minority and reaps intense fear of triple discrimination.

4. Offer your assistance with couples counseling or family counseling when the client wants to disclose or just discuss these issues

with someone else. The counselor's assistance may be needed for providing answers or support, and dealing with possible emotional ramifications.

CHAPTER SIX

Heterosexuality and HIV/AIDS

According to the CDC (1999), 19% of the newly diagnosed cases of African American adult and/or adolescents with AIDS are reported in the exposure category of heterosexual behaviors. HIV/AIDS is rapidly spreading into the African American heterosexual community. Although some of the HIV/AIDS concerns of the African American heterosexual client are similar if not the same as those of the drug abuser and the homosexual client, there are a few issues that may be unique. These unique issues are with respect to the African American that is non-gay and perhaps non-substance abusing. Consequently, some of the primary areas of concern for this population are disclosure, emotional issues, and the availability of adequate and appropriate HIV/AIDS services and programs. The objective of this chapter is to highlight the primary concerns of heterosexual African American men and women who are impacted by HIV/AIDS.

This chapter is designed to help the reader gain a stronger level of knowledge of how HIV/AIDS impacts heterosexual African American men and women. It should heighten the reader's level of sensitivity toward this population. It should also help them identify and understand some of the concerns that are different for heterosexual African Americans with HIV/AIDS. In addition, this chapter will provide the readers with many suggestions that can help improve the quality of life for the heterosexual African American who has HIV/AIDS.

DISCLOSURE

Once the acceptance of a diagnosis sinks in, so does the acceptance that other sexual partners, past and future, may be affected. For many African Americans, disclosure of an HIV/AIDS diagnosis can be extremely difficult. Disclosure to family and friends can be difficult enough, again because of the stigmas and the shame, but disclosure to a sexual partner who they may have passed the disease on to can be also traumatic.

This fear of disclosure can be coupled with guilt and shame. It is not unusual for the person with HIV/AIDS to avoid telling the sex partner about the diagnosis for a dangerously long period of time, if at all. It is not unusual for many individuals to find out they have been exposed to or infected with the virus, through other people, rather than through the person who infected them.

African Americans with HIV/AIDS also have trouble with disclosing their diagnosis to future partners who they have not yet had sex with. Some continue to have sex, with or without a condom, and still do not tell the partner. They often avoid telling them they have HIV/AIDS because of fear of rejection. They may feel "no one would want to have anything to do with them." It is not unusual for some African Americans with HIV/AIDS to avoid having sexual relationships completely, rather than disclose their diagnosis and risk rejection.

Some of these individuals choose to only have sexual relationships with others who also have an HIV/AIDS diagnosis. They often think it is alright to have unprotected sex if both parties have HIV/AIDS. This is a fallacy. There are various strains of the virus, therefore, persons with HIV/AIDS having unprotected sex with other people with HIV/AIDS can be further infecting each other. All of these issues can be overwhelming, depressing and stressful, thereby complicating their lives and the lives of others.

HETEROSEXUAL AFRICAN AMERICAN MEN WITH HIV/AIDS

First, we will focus on the issues of heterosexual African American men by addressing the various ways these men react to diagnosis and treatment. These reactions include being overly concerned about stigmas of homosexuality, their own issues of homophobia, resistance and embarrassment in accepting social programs and services, and the avoidance of certain service-providing facilities.

This section ends with a discussion of emotional issues that often occur in this male population. These issues include resistance to counseling and crisis intervention, avoidance of support systems, and issues of manhood. This section also uncovers common thoughts about condom usage and safer sex. It will discuss some of the reasons many of these men refuse to use condoms.

STIGMAS OF HOMOSEXUALITY

Because HIV/AIDS was originally associated with homosexuality, it continues to maintain that stigma within the African American community. Couple that stigma with the traditional resistance to homosexuality and homophobia in the African American community and many adverse effects can occur.

One of the strongest concerns of non-gay African American men who are diagnosed with HIV/AIDS is the overriding fear that "others will think that he is gay" because of the diagnosis. This fear is often transferred into intense anger and resentment and may intensify already existing feelings of homophobia. Many African American non-gay men, once diagnosed with HIV, become more vocal of their dislike for gays in order to further assure others and themselves that they are not gay.

Unfortunately, he is often so afraid of being thought of as gay that he avoids seeking adequate mental and physical help, support and services. It is not uncommon for non-gay African American men to avoid going to HIV-related clinics and agencies simply because gay individuals may also be there. As an African American man, his own prejudices may be so strong against gays that he resents any possible similarities that they may share, including their HIV/AIDS diagnosis.

From a psychological perspective it may be important for this client to explore his fears, angers, and issues of sexual identity. He may need to be assured of both his manhood and his heterosexuality. The client may be extremely resistant to therapy because he may consider it to be a sign of weakness or an infringement on his masculinity, and therefore, perpetuate his fear of being "thought of as gay."

AVAILABLE SERVICES

Historically, the majority of individuals who have been infected and impacted by HIV/AIDS have been part of the White and/or gay communities. Consequently, these communities are more experienced and pro-active in dealing with the HIV/AIDS issues and providing HIV/AIDS services. They have developed very effective and successful agencies and systems to help individuals live with the disease. Unfortunately, non-gay African American men often do not feel comfortable accessing these systems and services. Because of this discomfort, they will often avoid seeking adequate help, for fear of being connected with the gay community.

Many non-gay African American HIV/AIDS clients express feelings of loneliness and isolation. This is partly the consequence of the "absence of a supportive environment." This "absence" has influenced the non-gay individuals to remain isolated in their own community until other services or programs are provided. Without having an African American and non-gay supportive environment to identify with, these individuals can be not only isolated from AIDS-related issues and services but also from AIDS prevention and education (Jue & Kain, 1989). Some AIDS impacted clients experience "feelings of self-hatred" coupled with "increased desperation and alienation from society (Aoki, 1989)."

ACCEPTANCE

Once the individual has been diagnosed with HIV and is beginning to face it, his knowledge and level of acceptance begins to set in. This level of acceptance may manifest itself with signs of shame and embarrassment. The shame of having contracted such a "controversial" disease can often be overwhelming. With the stigma of homosexuality lurking in the background, the reality of having contracted the disease through sexual, even though heterosexual, behaviors can instill large levels of shame with an often proud and religious African American man.

This shame is felt with respect to his family, friends, the church, the community, and especially with women. Unfortunately, this shame is exhibited through depression and isolation. It is not unusual for this individual to shut himself off from what could very well be his most valued asset ... his support system.

This client needs to have the love and support of his family and friends in order to better cope with the many realities of having HIV. If he continues to isolate and sink into depression, his physical and mental health can be jeopardized. It is not unusual for some of these individuals to increase drinking and drug usage in order to "cope" with the depression as a way to "feel better."

COUNSELING AND CRISIS INTERVENTION

African American men are traditionally not interested in seeking counseling or psychological help because they often see counseling as a sign of weakness. Most of the men who seek counseling are either extremely depressed and referred to a counselor by another professional or they are in a crisis situation where they are desperate for help. They have usually spent a long period of time trying to deal with their issues on their own and have been unsuccessful. Unfortunately, by the time they seek professional help, the situations and/or issues are more severe or magnified.

The following may be important for a counselor to remember:

1. From a counseling perspective it may be important for this client to be assured of his "manhood" and heterosexuality.
2. The client may be extremely resistant to therapy and therefore may be the hardest

client to keep. Assure him, when he is ready
or when he needs you, you will try to be
there for him.

3. The counselor must also be sensitive to his
issues about being "around a lot of gays,"
when seeking HIV related services. The
counselor may have to help him to find support and services in areas where he is more
comfortable.

4. After trust is built and a solid client-counselor relationship is built, the counselor may
be able to help him deal with any anger or
identity issues as well as the possibility of
any prejudice towards gays.

<u>CONDOMS AND</u>
<u>AFRICAN AMERICAN MEN</u>

Avoidance of condom usage is also a big issue for
many non-gay African American men, for various reasons.
The primary reason seems to be the perception that the
physical feeling during intercourse is not as good. Another
reason seems to be that the condoms are too small or too
tight. Some men have complained that the need for a condom affects the spontaneity or romance of the situation. It
is also not unusual for some African American men to be
fearful that their mate may suspect they are seeing more
than one woman if they use a condom to protect her.

Regardless of the reason, protected sex is a must for
all parties involved. These men should be counseled and

encouraged to protect any individual who they may choose to become intimate with, along with disclosing their HIV/AIDS status. Additionally, they may need adequate safer-sex education, counseling, and guidance. These male clients also need to protect themselves from further HIV infection from women.

HETEROSEXUAL WOMEN AND HIV/AIDS

The concerns and issues that surface with heterosexual women diagnosed with HIV must also be explored. The rate of heterosexual and non-IV-drug using women who are getting infected by bisexual or heterosexual men is increasing.

As mentioned earlier, it is not uncommon for these women to be completely unaware that their partner is a carrier of the virus until they themselves are diagnosed. Many women are not aware of the possibility of their partner being bisexual, having had a relationship with another party, or of any dangers from their partner's previous sex or drug history.

The first part of this section is a discussion on the denial of African American women who are "at-risk" and issues about condom usage. Included in this section are discussions on self-esteem, the "extinct black man myth," and the fear of rejection from future men.

The last part of the chapter points out other issues that surface when working with this population, including prostitution, differences in medical concerns, substance abuse, children, isolation, self-care, anger at and trust in men, and support systems.

AT "RISK"

Again, due to the stigma that HIV/AIDS is a gay White disease, many African American women do not think that they are at risk. This is especially true for women who think they are in a relationship with a man who is not gay. Most women do not consider the fact that men who have sex with women and men who do not have an IV drug history could still be HIV positive. This denial by women, thinking they are not "at risk," can be extremely dangerous and life threatening.

ANGER, MISTRUST, AND DEPRESSION

Once diagnosed, the issues at hand may be shock and denial, coupled with intense anger and mistrust toward their mate and sometimes all men in general. Their own diagnosis may also be the way of finding out their partner had been cheating, using drugs, or is bisexual. Many African American women find the mistrust and anger is overwhelming. It is not unusual for some women to mistrust and become angry with all men who may come into their lives. Some African American women are so angry they want to physically hurt the man who infected them.

Severe levels of depression may also surface. This depression can be also dangerous to the woman. It can impair her level of self-esteem. Many African American women begin to think, because of HIV/AIDS, they will never have a meaningful relationship again. They begin to think "no one will want them." For women who have not had any children, the thought of never having a child or the risk of having a child with HIV can add to the depression.

Fear of loneliness and unworthiness can severely impair their quality of life because rather than risk rejection from a man, some of these women choose not to get into another relationship at all. Isolation can become a danger-ous result of these feelings. It is not unusual for these women to isolate themselves from family, friends, and men.

CONDOMS AND AFRICAN AMERICAN WOMEN

Once African American women begin to accept life with HIV, they are faced with the decision of having inti-mate relationships again. The loneliness may become unbearable, but the risk of being rejected may become even more unbearable. Along with the decision to have a rela-tionship again comes the issue of requiring him to wear a condom and disclosing her HIV status.

Many African American women have bought into the myth that the "black man is becoming extinct" or there "aren't enough black men for all of the women" or "they are all in prison or gay." Unfortunately, these thoughts can encourage a woman's fear of loneliness. These thoughts can also impair the quality of her decisions in choosing a prospective mate.

Once she has decided to have a man in her life, the risk of losing him becomes so overwhelming that she may be reluctant to disclose her HIV status. And because many African American men are against using condoms, she may also be reluctant in requiring him to wear a condom for fear he may reject her.

Of course the lower the self-esteem and the deeper the depression that a woman is in, the more severe these issues become. Therefore, improving the self-esteem, self-worth, and self-empowerment are paramount to the quality of life for African American women.

CHILDREN AND SELF-CARE

Once the woman has adjusted to the initial shock, one of the primary concerns that seem to be prevalent and consistent within African American women who have HIV/AIDS is concern for the welfare of her children, should she become unable to care for them. Historically, African American women have been taught to "take care of everything." They are accustomed to taking care of the house, the kids, a man, a job, and much more, and usually all at the same time. Unfortunately, she often neglects herself in the process. It is not uncommon for an African American woman to ignore her own feelings and needs in order to assure her children are taken care of.

How she is or is not dealing with the virus is often dependent on the well-being of the children. If her children are "OK," be it financially or emotionally, it is usually much easier for her to deal with the various issues about her well-being.

Therefore, it may be primarily important for the counselor to be prepared to help her gain peace of mind and security for her children. It may even be necessary to work with the children or refer the children to someone for help. In order for the counselor to truly get the client in a "place" where she is able to work on individual issues, the children will have to come first in the mind of both the client and the counselor. This mind-set is extremely important in developing trust and confidence in the helping relationship.

PROSTITUTION/SEX WORK

Due to the nature of drug abuse and addiction many of the heterosexual African American women who contract HIV/AIDS, may also have histories of prostitution and/or promiscuous sex. It is not only important for the helping professional to be mindful of the possible drug addiction but to also be willing to work with the women on their issues of sexuality, in which case the professional needs to be non-judgmental and sensitive.

Many of these women choose prostitution as their only means of survival in a very tough world. Some use it as a means to get more drugs. Others may be using prostitution as their only way to feel loved and wanted. Much professional work may be needed in order to help that individual with self-worth, especially in light of also having an HIV/AIDS diagnosis.

SUPPORT

Where these women would have traditionally sought support for their problems with their family or friends, due to the surrounding circumstances they often feel ashamed and inadequate, thereby holding in the truth and eventually feeling depressed, alone, and resentful. These women are also apt to experience "anger, betrayal, loss of trust, and fear for their own health and that of their children (Jue & Kain, 1989)."

Another one of the major differences between men and women with HIV/AIDS has to do with medical problems, because many women with HIV/AIDS develop various kinds of gynecological problems that can be long-term and reoccurring. Because of the nature of these types of problems, African American women seem to find great comfort in discussing both medical and personal issues with other African American women.

Support groups made up of only women are very successful at helping women to deal with the disease. Because the majority of the HIV/AIDS related support group services available are dedicated to individuals in drug recovery or gay men, the African American woman with HIV/AIDS doesn't have a comfortable place to talk and share with others who can identify with her issues as a woman or a mother with HIV. The woman-to-woman bonding and sharing environment can be both helpful and therapeutic. Women tend to have very loving and supportive groups when carefully designed and facilitated.

CHAPTER SEVEN

The Caregiver & HIV/AIDS

It is not only the person who is infected with the virus who is seriously impacted by HIV/AIDS. There is a host of others who must also be considered. In this chapter we will look at the main issues and concerns of both the professional and non-professional caregivers. These caregivers are an extremely important part of the needed support system for the person with HIV/AIDS.

THE PROFESSIONAL CAREGIVERS

The professional caregivers are usually medical and social services personnel, as well as mental health and government agency personnel. These caregivers include doctors, nurses, social workers, case managers, counselors, outreach workers, HIV educators, hospital, agency and clinical administrative staff, and any others who come in contact with the HIV/AIDS population in a professional capacity.

This discussion on the professional caregiver first points out issues of setting boundaries, ineffective emotional attachment and client dependency. Second, this chapter discusses burn-out, multiple-grief, cultural bias, and the referral process.

SETTING BOUNDARIES

It is extremely important for the professional caregiver to learn how to set and keep appropriate relationship boundaries with their client. The African American HIV/AIDS client is often reluctant to trust outside help. Therefore, once they have built a relationship with a professional person who they like and trust, the client may have expectations above and beyond the requirements of that person's responsibilities or capabilities. It is not unusual for the client to ask the professional to help them with issues unrelated to that professional's expertise to avoid having to trust yet another person.

Because this population very often has multiple needs and because the professional relationship can extend for many months and years, the professional must be very careful in not allowing the professional relationship to extend into a private relationship. When a caring professional has known a client for a long time and in some cases has learned the intimate details of a client's life, the professional may find themselves becoming too much of a friend rather than just a professional. With that friendship can come a host of ethical, professional, and moral dilemmas that include ineffective emotional attachment, and the client becoming overly dependent and less independent.

INEFFECTIVE EMOTIONAL ATTACHMENT

All professionals should have genuine caring feelings for their clients. However, when those feelings become too personal, the effectiveness of the client's care and the effectiveness of the professional's work are jeopardized. Working in the field of HIV is very serious and often stressful. If a professional has also become too emotionally attached to a client then the work can become even more stressful. Should that client become ill or have some other major problems occur, the professional may be too personally involved to continue to work effectively.

The professional runs the risk of excessive worry, becoming depressed, or losing focus on what their responsibilities include. In extreme cases, this could be compromising to their own mental health and personal well-being. Professionals must be careful not to let their involvement and care interfere with their own personal, family, and home life.

CLIENT DEPENDENCY

The many issues of battling HIV/AIDS, as well as the many other avenues of the African Americans life, can be numerous. The person with HIV/AIDS must learn to take responsibility for themselves as much as they reasonably and adequately can. They must become knowledgeable and proactive in the management of their health and life.

If the professional does not establish and keep boundaries, the client may become overly dependent on the professional and less dependent on themselves to the point of not managing their own well being. Therefore, the professional should avoid overextending into areas where the client must learn to do for themselves.

Furthermore, HIV/AIDS is growing in the African American community at alarming rates. Due to medical improvements, these individuals are living longer and healthier than ever before. Many of the clinics and agencies are overloaded with clients and understaffed with employees. The need for professionals in the field is huge. Therefore, clients must be empowered to do as much as they can, within their knowledge base and power, to help insure quality maintenance and management.

If professional caregivers are doing things the clients could be doing for themselves, it robs the client of opportunities to learn to be more independent. It also increases the work load of the professionals. There are not enough professionals in the field to handle all of the many issues they may encounter.

BURN-OUT

Working in the field of HIV/AIDS is extremely challenging and working with African Americans in the field of HIV/AIDS can be even more challenging. Heavy workloads, long days, difficult issues, difficult cases, and intense feelings can all add up to tired, stressed, and worn-out professionals. The end result is called burn-out. It is when an individual gets to a point they can no longer be effective in their work due to overwork and overstress. In many cases, they simply have to change jobs or change fields of work.

Professionals must learn to take care of themselves physically, mentally, and emotionally. Physically, they need to get adequate rest, nutrition, and exercise, just as they would expect their patients to do. Mentally, they need to keep current on any changes in the field that may make their work easier and more effective. Emotionally, they should set appropriate boundaries to avoid intense attachment, depression, and anxiety that may flow into their personal time, energy, and space.

It is perfectly alright for a professional in any stressful field to seek professional help for themselves because stress can occur in anyone, in any profession. It is paramount that the professional get help, to avoid the ramifications of burn-out.

MULTIPLE GRIEF AND
THE CAREGIVER

The rate of death for African Americans with AIDS is declining. Unfortunately, however, for various reasons there are still AIDS-related deaths occurring. For those professionals who have been in the HIV/AIDS field for a number of years, the number of clients who have died during one's professional career may become overwhelming.

Another difficult issue for the professional caregiver is dealing with the many deaths of people they have known and cared for in their professional capacity. This type of grief is called multiple grief. Even when the professional is the best at setting and keeping emotional boundaries, he or she is not immune from hurting and dealing with the issues of grief. In the field of HIV/AIDS, it is often multiple grief.

People working in the HIV/AIDS field should, and usually do, have great compassion for their clients. The need for self-care when grieving, is normal, realistic, and highly possible. Once again, the professionals must learn to take care of themselves and recognize when the grieving is manageable, or when they are overwhelmed. Sometimes the loss of a client can trigger memories of prior clients or personal losses. It is not unusual for some professionals to become angry with themselves or others for perhaps not being able to "do more" or "save the person's life."

They must learn to seek counseling or support from other professionals, if need be. They must be able to address their feelings in the most effective and helpful ways, in order to get on with their life and career. If a professional person working with HIV/AIDS is unable to deal with such issues, then it is understandable if that person chooses to seek another field of work. They would be of no use to their clients, their family, or to themselves if they are overwhelmed with grief and depression.

CULTURAL BIAS

In working with African Americans with HIV/AIDS, professionals in the field must be aware, knowledgeable, and sensitive to the needs and issues of various sub-cultures within that population. Some of these sub-groups include:

African Americans
African Americans living with HIV/AIDS
Gay African Americans
Bisexual African Americans
African American substance abusers and addicts
African Americans with prison histories
African American sex addicts and prostitutes
African Americans with religious issues
African Americans in lower socio-economic groups
Homophobic African Americans

It is imperative for professionals in the field to be honest with themselves and with others if they do not feel they can be sensitive, caring, fair, impartial, and non-discriminatory to any of these sub-groups. It is very difficult for professionals in any capacity to be effective in the caring profession if they have cultural biases or prejudicial feelings toward their client.

Harboring these kinds of thoughts and feelings can be dangerous to the clients' well being, dangerous to the professional, and unethical to the profession. It is not unusual for some professionals to have strong personal issues with homosexuality or race. But if those issues have any adverse or unfair impact on the care, sensitivity, and effectiveness of their professional services, then that professional should refer the client to another professional who can better meet that individual's needs. In addition, that professional should honestly try to explore those feelings, become more educated, and hopefully overcome as much of their biases and prejudices they possibly can.

REFERRAL PROCESS

The African American population and especially the African American HIV/AIDS population is very tired of being shifted throughout the medical and political system from one service provider to another. Many times it cannot be avoided. A client needs to go to various medical specialists, depending on their physical needs. Or they may need various service providers, depending on their social and financial needs. Therefore, care and assistance must be taken when the professional refers the client to another professional. African Americans are very sensitive to being shuffled from one person in the system to another.

Tips for the referral of African American clients:

1. Explain the need for the referral so the client does not feel dumped or abandoned.
2. If possible, only refer clients to professionals who are culturally sensitive.
3. If possible, only refer to professionals who the profes-

sional can talk to and perhaps assist, personally or by tele-phone, when introducing to the client.

4. If possible (without overstepping boundaries), help the client with the issues that are within the professionals area of their expertise. Try to avoid yet another referral.

5. Follow-up on the referral to ensure the process was com-pleted. And if not, find out why.

THE NON-PROFESSIONAL CAREGIVERS

There are many non-professional individuals that find themselves working with and caring for African Americans with HIV/AIDS. These caregivers can include family members, significant others, church members, co-workers, support groups, friends and volunteers.

Because the HIV/AIDS epidemic impacted the White gay community in such devastating proportions, the primary non-professional caregiver was usually another gay individual or at least an individual who was sensitive to gay issues. Due to several other issues within the African American community, including homophobia and mis-edu-cation, this has not often been the case for many African Americans with HIV/AIDS.

Because of strong kinship bonds of many African American clients, the primary care-giver is very often the mother, sister, or other close family member. Historically, the African American family must be understood as being different than the stereotypical nuclear family of "father, mother, and children."

The African American family can also include other combinations, such as the grandmother raising grandchildren or the single mother raising her children or nieces and nephews. In addition, adult children are often still living with elderly parents. African American families often include cousins or children of friends and neighbors. Sometimes the African American family is extended towards uncles and aunts who are also living with their children and their parents.

Professional and non-professional caregivers, especially those in the fields of counseling and social services, must be aware of the diversity of the African American family systems in order to better understand some of the issues of the client and their non-professional support system. It is important for the caregiver to get a clear understanding of what constitutes a "family" to the client. They need to have a clear understanding of those considered to be family members of the client who are most significant and supportive. It is not unusual for a child who is raised by their grandmother to refer to that person as their mother.

Family issues, emotions, and concerns are often the root of some of the depression, anxiety, and subsequent inadequate self-care for many African Americans with HIV/AIDS. Such issues include client concerns for family, family fear of infection, family shame and conflicts, grief, and stress.

CLIENT CONCERNS FOR FAMILY

When an African American individual begins to require care from family members, it isn't uncommon for the infected person to become more concerned with the issues of the caregiver than concerned with the issues of themselves. They often become worried about how their HIV/AIDS situation is affecting the primary caregiver or their significant other. The client is often very well aware of how difficult life may have been for that individual in the past and is now concerned that their HIV/AIDS issues will only further complicate that person's life.

The client's primary issue may be to avoid burdening a parent with care for a sick adult, or perhaps adding tremendous medical care expenses to an already low-income lifestyle. The client may also be concerned with the expense of burial that may be left in the hands of the family member.

Because of the stigmas of the HIV/AIDS disease, it is not uncommon for a client to avoid leaning on family for fear of adding shame and disgrace to the family name or to family members. Clients should learn to work through such feeling and issues with professionals in the field, such as counselors and social workers.

FAMILY FEAR OF INFECTION

Even in today's modern society of education and information, there are still a host of African American individuals who do not know the facts about the spread of

HIV/AIDS. There are still many individuals who erroneously think the AIDS virus can be transmitted in ways such as using eating and drinking materials, shaking hands, or sitting on commode seats. Many individuals are still fearful of others who have the disease, even when there is no known risk of infection.

Unfortunately, this population includes many of the non-professional caregivers such as family and friends. This uneducated fear may cause the caretaker to say and do hurtful things to the client with HIV/AIDS. Caregivers need to become educated or trained by professionals in the field, or through current, accurate, and reliable literature. By gaining knowledge, much of the stress for a caregiver can be eliminated.

FAMILY SHAME AND CONFLICTS

The family, particularly the primary caretaker, may also be experiencing some levels of shame for their HIV/AIDS-related loved-one. The shame may be directed toward the individual because of their feelings toward homosexuality or drug abuse.

The very religious family caregiver may be dealing with shame due to religious feelings about homosexuality and drug abuse. Their inability to accept some very important components of the client's life can cause constant internal and external struggles between the caregiver and the client. These types of struggles can make the care-giving process stressful and perhaps more detrimental.

Sometimes the shame is directed toward themselves and is often coupled with blame. It is not unusual for the parents that raised the infected individual to blame themselves for some of the problems the client has incurred. Some parents blame themselves for perhaps "doing something wrong" as a parent, or perhaps "not being able to spend enough time with the child when they were young."

The family that is very spiritual (not necessary just religious) is usually the most supportive, forgiving, and accepting of surrounding issues of the client's lifestyle. It is helpful for counselors and social workers to find out what a family's spiritual belief system is like and, if need be, help them to tap into that belief system for strength and empowerment.

In some cases the family is struggling with having to share caregiving responsibilities with the gay significant other. The primary issue of concern for the African American client may be dealing with possible conflict between the person's homophobic family members and the gay lover or friend. It is not uncommon for the client to be deeply concerned that the family may mistreat or ignore the pain and emotional needs of their gay loved one who is also involved in his or her care.

Insensitive family members might not be as accepting of the homosexual relationship. In their pain and anger, they may resort to verbal conflict with the client and the client's friends. Family therapy and counseling could help in these areas.

It is important for the counselor to be able to antici-pate such intense dynamics. It may even be necessary for the counselor to help the caregiver work through some of the anger and pain that is also associated with both the phys-ical and financial burden that the infected individual may cause.

Being a caregiver for persons with HIV/AIDS can be a very long and difficult process. The caregiver may be dealing with fear of losing the person, the pain of watching them suffer, the technicalities of the social services and grief. The counselor should be familiar with stress reduc-tion techniques or education and information regarding wellness and mental health care.

GRIEF

Fortunately for many of the African American with HIV/AIDS, the rate of death is declining. But for some, another issue with the African American family and spiritu-ality can be death and the grieving process. For the previ-ously mentioned reasons, the ways in which some African Americans grieve needs to be understood.

It is important to understand that culturally African Americans may grieve in many different ways when com-pared to mainstream Americans. For some African Americans the person who has died is often considered to be "no longer suffering" and is finally going to a "place of peace." Some African American religions believe death is a "celebration" for the person's "home going" to God.

Because the client and their caregivers are often dealing with issues of illness, and perhaps anticipatory death, the counselor and social workers should be able to help explore and discuss their cultural beliefs with regard to such matters. This may lead to dealing with the client's coping methods, suicidal risks, and decisions about the use of artificial life support systems (Jue & Kain, 1989). Because of various levels of education, cultural beliefs, and religious beliefs, such topics are often foreign and difficult for many African Americans to face.

STRESS

As mentioned previously, with regard to the professional caregiver who is helping an African American with HIV/AIDS, it can also be very stressful for the non-professional caregiver. Family and loved ones must learn to recognize when they are stressed out, tired and overwhelmed. They must learn to take care of themselves by getting adequate rest, nutrition and exercise, as well as proper mental health help if needed. The non-professional caregiver must be able to allow others to help them if need be, and not try to take all of the responsibilities on alone. After all, they cannot be of any assistance to other family members if they are stressed out and ineffective.

Non-professional caregivers must learn to know their limits. And they must also be aware that in many cases they may not have the knowledge and expertise to provide many types of adequate care. There may be the occasion when they will have to admit they can no longer provide the kind of care the client needs and turn them over to an appropriate professional. This can be a very difficult decision, but in many cases it is the best decision for both the client and the caregiver.

Part III:

The Holland-Blackwell Model, External Systems

CHAPTER EIGHT

External Systems and HIV

When investigating the many issues of the African American client with respect to this devastating epidemic, it is necessary to look at several aspects of our society. These external systems help us to understand implications significant to the African American client, including medical healthcare, economics and politics.

MEDICAL HEALTH CARE SYSTEM

Due to the lower socioeconomic status of many of the African American individuals who are infected with HIV/AIDS, adequate medical healthcare can be a difficult and emotional issue. For those who cannot afford private practitioners and private hospitals or those who do not have medical insurance, the only alternative is often county hospitals and clinics, or various non-profit clinics and institutions.

NON-PROFIT FACILITIES

These institutions are generally funded by government-regulated grants and medical insurance, fund-raising sources, or private donations. When this is the case, the funds available are often limited and usually not enough to meet the needs and the demands of this ever growing population. When funds are limited, many times the services and medication are also limited.

In major cities where the HIV/AIDS population is usually larger, the county facilities may be the best place for the HIV/AIDS-related individual to go. These facilities usually have more experience with such cases than the average private physician office.

It is essential for all individuals involved in the HIV/AIDS crisis within the African American population to understand the often seen connection between many African Americans and some medical health care systems. Many times, due to limited funding the quality of care and the abilities and size of the staff are also limited. Many of these facilities are small and often crowded. The number of examination rooms may not be adequate and the size of the staff may also be small. The number of qualified doctors, nurses, technicians, and other professionals is often inadequate to serve the size of the population of patients.

CULTURALLY SENSITIVE STAFF AND FACILITY

The training of the staff is also expensive. Many of these professionals are not culturally sensitive to the issues and concerns of the African American HIV/AIDS community. Cultural sensitivity training of the staff is essential in working with this population. Professionals must learn effective ways of communicating, working with, and meeting the needs of the African American client. Without proper sensitivity training many clients are discriminated against, treated unfairly, insulted, embarrassed, or just misunderstood.

When a client is misunderstood, the professional may also mis-diagnose certain ailments, offer inappropriate referrals, make inaccurate assumptions, and therefore provide inappropriate care. The ending result of such infractions can cause many African Americans to become mistrustful, angry, shameful, and therefore unwilling to continue seeking medical help.

To avoid such feelings, many African Americans would rather not seek medical help than sit in an overcrowded and inadequately staffed medical facility and risk being mistreated. Unfortunately, without regular medical help, the patient's health may decline.

Another issue with respect to insensitivity may have to do with the operations of the facility itself. The hours of operation may be inflexible to those who cannot afford to miss work on a regular basis. The rules of not allowing children may be difficult for many parents to follow. The long waiting periods for getting prescriptions filled may be detrimental to one's health. The location of the facility may be difficult for those who do not have a car.

MEDICAL COMMUNICATION

Included with cultural insensitivity is insensitivity to surrounding issues of language, education, and communication. Many African Americans have a distinct way of communicating, known as Ebonics. The language of Ebonics is a reality in the African American community. It should be respected as an important part of the African American culture.

Professionals should become knowledgeable of the modes of communication within this population to avoid miscommunication and possible alienation. Also along with possible lower levels of education come lower levels of medical education. Professionals should take care in using medical terms, acronyms and descriptions. They should take care to ensure that the patient is truly understanding what the professional is saying. HIV/AIDS patients should ask questions if they are not sure of what the professional has said.

Patients may be experiencing feelings of humiliation and embarrassment from having to go to a county institution rather than a private doctor. It is not unusual for some African Americans to avoid these county and other non-profit facilities because they do not want to "accept charity."

CONFIDENTIALITY

Confidentiality of their diagnosis is also an issue. Many African Americans have great pride and do not want others to know they have HIV/AIDS. They are often fearful of being seen at certain HIV/AIDS known facilities due to the risk of losing confidentiality. All of these issues contribute to why many African Americans may not be seeking and therefore receiving the medical care they need.

Trust issues are also seen with respect to medical insurance companies. Another concern having to do with confidentiality may be regarding medical records and medical information. Those African Americans who do have jobs with medical insurance may be in fear of their diagnosis causing them to lose their benefits and even their jobs. Many of these individuals are not familiar with the laws and regulations against AIDS discrimination in the work force.

These individuals must learn about such laws and company policies to help reduce their level of fear and stress. Professionals should provide education and information regarding the rights of the patients. It may be necessary for the professional to provide education and information regarding the various medical systems and perhaps prepare the client for what they might encounter or expect to happen.

The client may need some general "wellness information" in order to understand and appreciate the value of taking care of themselves with early intervention. The client may be better able to deal with a "long day at the clinic" if they understand the importance of the medical care as well as the potential issues and problems.

ECONOMIC SYSTEM

There also seems to be a correlation between income levels, levels of education, and health status (Goodwin, 1992; Fullilove, 1990). Approximately 85% of the reported AIDS cases are in metropolitan areas with 500,000 or more population (CDC, 1997).

African Americans that reside in these areas are often victims of both historical and current oppression and racism. The ramifications of such oppression are most often seen at the economic level. The primary interest of these individuals is usually related to basic survival. Such issues include food, rent and safety. In such cases, preventive health care may not be considered as important at the time.

"When life is a day-to-day struggle to balance single parenting, unemployment, or working two or three jobs, dealing with substandard education, lack of money, teenage pregnancy, and homelessness, all very present realities in many of our communities, AIDS seems a distant specter (Mitchell, 1992)." The end result is often behaviors and practices such as drug addiction and high-risk sexual activity. Those who are infected and at lower economic levels run a higher risk of using up their funds on medical care and are also subject to discrimination in employment and housing (Goodwin, 1992).

SOCIAL SERVICES

The HIV/AIDS related social services process may be new to many African Americans. They may not be aware of the types of services that are available for HIV/AIDS-related clients.

The effective counselor, case manager, or social worker should be aware that many times an African American client may be seeking their advice on various social services such as Welfare, Social Security, food and clothing assistance, legal assistance, housing assistance and other sources of financial assistance. Such professionals should have a working knowledge and current list of all related financial services. It would be a good idea to have a list of the various agencies or service providers to refer to the client.

The professional must be willing to help the client with many of these issues in order to help build the trusting relationship that is needed for further growth and development with respect to more tangible and intangible issues. It is extremely difficult for a client to concentrate on health care if they are overwhelmed with basic survival issues.

Professionals should not ignore or underestimate such issues. If a client is more concerned with paying their rent then taking their medication, the professional should not assume that the individual is in denial about their HIV/AIDS status. If a client is not complying to their medical regiment, professionals should investigate what else may be going on in that person's life that might be more important at the time.

POLITICAL SYSTEM

The history of the African American from slavery, through the civil rights movements and even today, has a direct impact on the political implications of the African American client. This political system encompasses not only racism and discrimination at the education level, the unemployment level, the economic conditions, and the living conditions, but also the emotional stages of the client.

RACISM

Because of the client's perceptions, beliefs, and experiences with their historical and current political situation there tends to be a direct impact on such feelings of anger, distrust, shame, and fear. It is not uncommon for an African American HIV/AIDS client to feel that AIDS is "just one more problem that they have to deal with in this society."

The professional needs to not only be aware of the impact of racism on the African American client with HIV/AIDS, but he or she must take it seriously and not overlook its implications or its importance in understanding and relating to their clients.

The professional must not let his or her own issues of racism and prejudice get involved and therefore discount the client's perceptions, feelings, and reality. Whatever the client's feelings are on the subject, they are real and important to that African American client. If an African American client is experiencing rage and is "blaming the White world for everything," the professional should be able to discuss these feelings with the client.

Most African Americans would be referring to institutional racism. Such feelings and thoughts are common among many disenfranchised African Americans, and the quality of medical care should not be compromised because of it. If the professional cannot empathetically and sensitively work through such issues with the patient, the client may perceive the counselor is not respectful and perhaps incapable of understanding. In such cases, a referral to another professional may be needed.

GENOCIDE

There are various theories on how the AIDS virus came to be. One of those theories commonly held by many African Americans, is that AIDS is a form of political genocide. A political issue for many African Americans is the belief that the HIV/AIDS epidemic was purposely developed by the White heterosexual culture as a selective genocide to destroy the gay and African American cultures. Due to the historical oppression of African Americans and homosexuals in this country, this is a reality to many and should be take seriously (Croteau et al., 1993).

How the virus came to be is, of course important but that issue should be left in the hands of researchers and advocates. It should not be the prevailing concern for health care professionals or the patients. Quality medical and personal healthcare should take precedence. The HIV/AIDS professional should not lose focus on their primary responsibility of providing care and services. If the client brings this issue up, the professional should not take this type of issue as a personal attack or attempt to change that person's mind or react with anger. Whether the professional agrees or disagrees should not compromise the care or sensitivity required for the client.

GAY POLITICAL POWER

Over the past decade HIV/AIDS and gay rights have become extremely powerful and influential topics on the political forefront. As a result, the number of supporters have grown, as well as, the political clout. Along with this gay political power has come strong HIV/AIDS-related legislation, with improved education, funding, and services. Because HIV/AIDS began as a predominately gay and White epidemic, most of the benefits of this power structure initially affected the gay and White HIV/AIDS community.

Unfortunately, an African American gay political counterpart has not yet developed. Because of the stigmatization and homophobia within the African American community, these new gay political forces are predominantly non-African American. Consequently the political and economic advances and benefits for gays and HIV/AIDS that were accomplished are slow to reach the African American client.

The developing strength of the African American political power system at large is carrying most of the influence toward the HIV/AIDS battle within the African American community in addition to many other political, social, medical, and economic issues that affect African Americans.

The issue of political power effects the client and the professional by way of providing funding and legislation to support the much-needed and culturally appropriate programs, services, and research for this African American HIV/AIDS population.

CHAPTER NINE
The Counseling System

One of the most important and influential systems the African American HIV/AIDS-related client may come in contact with is the counseling system. This counseling system is often very new to African Americans. Almost all of the care-giving professionals in this field at some point in time find themselves in the role of being some type of counselor to the client. These professionals can include social workers, nurses, case managers, outreach works and doctors.

These professionals may find themselves in the position to provide counseling on a variety of topics. Care must be given, however, in providing counseling to clients when the professional is neither trained, nor experienced in handling a particular type of counseling. For example, a social worker should not give medical advice and a case manager should not provide psychotherapy.

Because African American clients often have difficulty in developing trust with professionals, once the client has developed a trusting relationship with the professional the client tends to lean on that one trusted professional extensively. This can be dangerous if the professional is asked to provide advice or counseling beyond their professional training or expertise.

Clear boundaries must be set for the job responsibilities of each type of counseling. Clear distinctions must be made between medical and social services/case management, legal, mental health, pastoral, and group counseling. These professionals must be able to clearly explain what type of counseling they are providing to the client and they must stay within their expertise. Clients can be damaged by inappropriate or ineffective counseling. Inaccurate information can cause medical and emotional problems.

MEDICAL COUNSELING

This type of counseling should be provided by trained and licensed medical personnel, including such professionals as a doctor or nurse. They should give clients advice on such issues as formal diagnosis, physical health condition, medications, daily health regimens, wellness program, exercise and diet.

SOCIAL SERVICES/CASE MANAGEMENT COUNSELING

This type of counseling should be provided by a trained and experienced social worker or case manager. This individual should provide information and tracking for the various programs and services available to individuals with HIV/AIDS. Such information and services should cover financial aid, Social Security, food and shelter, education, child care, and referrals to other sources of help.

MENTAL HEALTH COUNSELING

This type of counseling should be provided by licensed, experienced and properly trained mental health counselors. This would include such professionals as psychologists, psychiatrists, psychotherapists, Licensed Professional Counselors (LPC), Licensed Chemical Dependency Counselors (LCDC) and Licensed Marriage and Family Therapy (LMFT) counselors. These professionals would help clients with mental health issues such as depression, grief, personality disorders, substance abuse and addiction and compulsive disorders.

The remainder of this chapter will deal with issues of mental health counseling. Over the past decade several researchers have assessed the needs of the African American HIV/AIDS client under the realm of cross-cultural counseling or minority issues (Aoki, 1989; Fullilove, 1990; Croteau et al., 1993). "All behavior, including that related to constructive action in the face of HIV and AIDS, occurs within the context of the individual's membership in particular social and cultural groups (Croteau et al., 1990; Croteau et al., 1993)." The counselor working with ethnic minority clients with HIV/AIDS and their families must be knowledgeable and sensitive to the client's cultural influences and values and how these values impact their behaviors.

It is essential that the counselor be able to "recognize the effects of social oppression directed toward these populations." Such issues could include negative attitudes toward homosexuals, institutional racism, and working with various social stigmas (Croteau et al., 1992).

Historically, African Americans have often exhibited much resistance to mental health counseling. The issue of resistance to the counseling process is often an important issue for the counselor to be able to understand and deal with. The primary reasons for such resistance are due to clients being unfamiliar with the mental health counseling process, mistrust, shame and pride, traditional expense, and culturally insensitive counselors.

UNFAMILIAR WITH THE MENTAL HEALTH COUNSELING PROCESS

It is common for the HIV/AIDS impacted African American who is seeking counseling to be unfamiliar with the mental health counseling process, expecting to receive social assistance, information and/or "concrete services" rather than engaging in a discussion of feelings (Jue & Kain, 1989).

Mental health counseling, also known as psychotherapy, is simply psychologically-based theories and techniques developed and used to help individuals work through emotional issues and various mental states of mind. Some issues can indeed become serious and require medical assistance from a doctor or psychiatrist. But most emotional issues can be facilitated by a licensed professional.

It is imperative that the counselor provide the client with a clear understanding of what mental health counseling is, how it should work, expectations and any other information that might help the client become familiar and comfortable with the process.

The client must understand HIV/AIDS is a lot to deal with and think about. Depression is not uncommon. Thoughts of suicide are not uncommon. Fighting substance abuse is not uncommon. Family and relationship issues are not uncommon. Grief is not uncommon. Fear, anger, confusion and denial, just to name a few, are not uncommon. The African American client must learn, it is perfectly healthy to seek mental health counseling to help make those years as manageable and fulfilling as possible.

From a counseling standpoint, denial (Fullilove, 1990) seems to be the major issue that perpetuates the problem of AIDS in the African American community. This denial exists in the infected and the non-infected, the families, the churches, the leaders and politicians and the community at large. Today, almost everyone knows someone impacted by HIV/AIDS, but many African Americans still don't want to talk about it.

The counselor must also be prepared to deal with "internalized negative stereotypes," while helping to improve the client's level of self-esteem. Low self-esteem is common, particularly with African Americans with HIV/AIDS, due to their history of oppression or stigmatization. It is important for the counselor to be interested in how oppression has influenced a client's difficulty with avoidance, trust and distrust, and resistance to self-disclosure (Jue & Kain, 1989).

MISTRUST, SHAME AND PRIDE

Many African Americans still believe an individual "must be crazy to get counseling" and avoid being associated with that stigma. There is great fear of being labeled as "retarded" or "psychotic," being institutionalized into a mental health hospital, or being over medicated with mental health medication. Many African Americans, because of historical racism, are distrusting of the mental health counseling system. They may consider seeking counseling as a threat to their independence and control.

Many African Americans may see counseling as a sign of relinquishing control of their life to someone else. It is often a difficult and emotional decision for African Americans to seek counseling, therefore the counselor should be aware that by the time the African American client comes in for services, he or she may be in a serious state or in some type of emotional crises.

There are also the issues of shame and embarrassment within the African American client. There is still the stigma that therapy is "a White thing," causing many African Americans shame and embarrassment when seeking mental health counseling. They don't want anyone to know they need mental health help. Confidentiality may be one of their biggest concerns.

It is not unusual for African Americans to be taught as children that "what goes on at home.....stays at home." Discussing "personal business with strangers" is often considered wrong and inappropriate in many African American families. Such feelings, thoughts and fears need to be explored and examined with many African American clients. Counselors may need to help clients by developing a stronger comfort level with such issues.

EXPENSE

Many African Americans find it difficult to think of mental health counseling as a necessity, and therefore are unwilling to spend very much money for the services. Even for African Americans who can afford the services, it is often difficult for them to commit to regular and especially long-term therapy if it will cost very much money.

Mental health professionals should investigate the various financial options that are available to individuals with HIV/AIDS. Some of these options may include insurance, Medicaid, HIV/AIDS-related funding and grants, government mental health facilities and substance abuse programs. Many of the HIV/AIDS programs and services provide mental health counseling, services, and financing for HIV/AIDS-related clients.

THE CULTURALLY SENSITIVE COUNSELOR

The key to finding mental health professionals for African Americans, as with any particular cultural group, is to find one who is culturally sensitive and culturally trained in working with that population.

HIV/AIDS in the African American community encompasses a complex array of physical, psychological, emotional and social issues. Because of this complexity, mental health counselors must be patient, flexible and extremely knowledgeable of several disciplines within the realm of African American sociology as well as psychology. Such disciplines may include chemical dependency, sexuality, depression, spirituality, racial identity, crises intervention and family therapy.

These mental health care providers must also be willing to move beyond the traditional roles of psychotherapy and at times also become teachers, consultants, career advisors and information referral systems. For the therapist, HIV/AIDS counseling can be stressful and long-term but can also become rewarding and meaningful. For the African American client it can become their conduit toward a quality of life.

When investigating the many emotional and social issues of African Americans with HIV/AIDS, the counselor must not only be aware of several aspects of our society which seem to affect the African American HIV/AIDS client, but must also be aware of themselves and their own issues of bias and prejudice.

How the African American culture views counseling is an important issue for the counselor to examine. The counselor must be sensitive to "social and familiar" roles with the client who is infected with AIDS (Jue & Kain, 1989). Research (Croteau et al., 1992) suggests that programs that incorporate such issues deserve more consideration among professionals who work with HIV/AIDS multicultural groups.

CHARACTERISTICS OF AFRICAN AMERICAN CLIENTS

Sue & Sue (1990) have conceptualized basic beliefs and values that have impacted the therapeutic practice of counseling African Americans. These group variables include:

1. The existence of an African American language, often known as Ebonics, as opposed to standard English.

2. African Americans tend to be group-oriented rather than individual-oriented. There is also a strong sense of extended family.

3. African Americans also tend to appreciate a concrete, tangible, structured approach to counseling.

4. Immediate goals that are short-term seem to work better with the African American client.

5. African Americans tend to be action-oriented.

6. The African American client may have a different appreciation for time and punctuality.

CHARACTERISTICS OF A CULTURALLY-SKILLED COUNSELOR

Sue and Sue (1990) believed that a counselor who is culturally skilled will have acquired specific attitudes and beliefs that are congruent with the following characteristics:

1. The culturally-skilled counselor is one who has moved from being culturally unaware to being aware and sensitive to his/her own cultural heritage and to valuing and respecting differences.

2. The culturally-skilled counselor is aware of his/her own values and biases, and how they may affect minority clients.

3. Culturally-skilled counselors are comfortable with differences that exist between themselves and their client in terms of race and beliefs.

4. The culturally-skilled counselor is sensitive to circumstances (personal biases, stages of ethnic identity, sociopolitical influences, etc.) that may dictate referral of the minority client to a member of his/her own race/culture or to another counselor, in general.

5. The culturally-skilled counselor acknowledges and is aware of his/her own racist attitudes, beliefs, and feelings (p. 167-168).

GROUP COUNSELING

There are basically two types of group counseling, process and support. The process group is usually a more therapeutic group that is specifically dealing with a particular mental health disorder or issue. Support group counseling, which is more of a forum for sharing information and feelings, has been found to be the most effective with many African Americans. The most successful have been among women and substance abusers with HIV/AIDS.

Group counseling is a very effective way of helping African Americans who are infected with HIV/AIDS, particularly if they are suffering from feelings of isolation and confusion. Many of these individuals profit from knowing they are "not alone." It often helps to have someone to talk to with similar issues.

The important thing for the counselor to remember is that homogeneity within the group is often very essential. The members of the group should have similar issues. When grouped with care and sensitivity, the African American group members tend to bond and grow much more effectively and positively.

It is usually more effective if all members of the group are not only HIV/AIDS diagnosed, but are also African American and, if possible, within the same socioeconomic level. Issues of race, discrimination, survival or hatred may need to be discussed.

It may also be important that the group members all be of the same sex. African American females with HIV/AIDS have many different issues than African

American males with HIV/AIDS and may feel uncomfortable discussing such issues in front of a man.   It may also be necessary to have a group with similar sexual preferences or sexual identity. Due to homophobia, it may be difficult to successfully mix non-gay men with gay men in a support group setting. Again, the issues are often very different.

Yet another concern may be with respect to substance abuse. It is usually best to have a separate HIV/AIDS support group for individuals that have substance abuse issues. Because of the complexity, substance abuse issues can be more important than HIV/AIDS issues at any point in time. It would be unfair to a non-substance abuser to spend a large amount of time working on the often overwhelming issues of the substance abuser.

<u>PASTORAL COUNSELING</u>

Traditionally, when faced with emotional or personal problems, many African Americans sought counseling from their church pastor. As mentioned in chapter five, the church and religion have been very powerful and influential in the African American community. Many African Americans still believe their pastor has all of the answers.

Appropriate and effective counseling advice from one's pastor can be very helpful when the pastor stays within his/her level of expertise. However, care must be taken. Counseling from anyone, including one's pastor and family, can be quite dangerous if they are advising someone on issues that are not within their level of expertise.

The Counseling System

Just as with medical and legal counseling, pastor's boundaries should be set with respect to expertise. Unqualified therapists should not do religious counseling and unqualified pastors should not do therapy. Many pastors are not trained in mental health disorders, emotional disturbances, sexual and racial identity issues, substance abuse counseling and therapy. Many pastors are not experienced in dealing with the current issues of HIV/AIDS, as well as the ramifications, the effects on the family or the effects on the African American community.

The most effective use of pastoral counseling, when the pastor is not also a licensed therapist, is for the client to use the information in addition to therapeutic counseling. This is often quite possible and quite effective if the two types of counseling are not in conflict with each other.

The issues of the African American who is impacted by HIV/AIDS are varied and complex. For one to be able to work with and help such an individual, the counselor must have an understanding of and an appreciation for the African American culture as it stands today as well as how that culture has been impacted by history, racism, and society. Some of these issues include myths, economics, politics, and medical care system. The counselor must also be able to deal with the culture specific issues with regard to family spirituality, homosexuality, drug usage, death and the client perspective to the counseling process. All of the above mentioned issues and concerns must be dealt with utmost sensitivity, knowledge, and respect.

Part IV:

Holistic Model for a Better Quality of Life

Holistic Pie

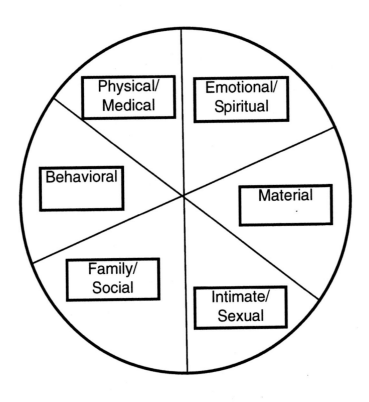

Physical/Medical

Emotional/Spiritual

Behavioral

Material

Family/Social

Intimate/Sexual

Holistic Model for a Better Quality of Life

CHAPTER TEN

The Holistic Model for a Better Quality of Life for African Americans and HIV/AIDS

The aim of this chapter is to present a holistic approach to life and living, designed to incorporate all of the unique and interdependent aspects of African Americans dealing with issues of HIV/AIDS, substance abuse and sexuality. This approach can be used by both professionals and non-professionals in the field. This approach can be used by individuals impacted by HIV/AIDS, including friends and family members. Additionally, this approach can also be utilized by any individuals dealing with long-term physical and mental health concerns.

The Holistic Model for a Better Quality of Life for African Americans and HIV/AIDS is a six-part model. Each area of the model needs to be addressed when working with HIV/AIDS issues with African Americans. In order to improve the quality of one's life, no area should be ignored. This holistic approach is critical in helping African Americans with HIV/AIDS for many reasons:

a. They contract the virus through many different ways within the community at alarming rates.
b. They have unique socio-economic and political issues, including oppression and discrimination.
c. They have many unique issues with respect to sexuality, including homophobia and shame.
d. They have many unique behavioral issues, including substance abuse and addiction.
e. They have many unique emotional issues, including mental health stigmas.

The goal of the model is to help African Americans impacted with HIV/AIDS take an active part in developing a quality life. It is designed to help African Americans become completely aware and in control of their life, healthcare and responsibilities with respect to healthy living. It is very much an individual wellness program.

It incorporates all areas of one's life. Many African Americans choose to give that responsibility to the doctors, fate, case managers or family members. Still others choose not to do anything but wait for a crisis or even death. This program is designed to provide individuals with self-awareness, development, control, and empowerment so they are better able to work with the HIV/AIDS professionals.

The six areas of the Holistic Model for a Better Quality of Life for African Americans with HIV/AIDS are simple enough to be explored by the individual with or without therapeutic help. However, it may be much easier and more successful if one can gain the assistance of a licensed professional. The professional can help the individual stay focused, consistent and provide additional insight the individual may be overlooking.

A good resource for the Holistic Model for a Better Quality of Life for African Americans with HIV/AIDS is this book. This book is a compilation of information, experience, expertise, and knowledge gained over ten years in working with this population. It is based on the Holland-Blackwell Model for Counseling Intervention for African Americans with HIV/AIDS. The information outlined in the book will help individuals address the many issues that may be needed to be addressed in order to have a better quality of life. However, this book is just a guide.

There are many books, pamphlets, magazines, and other forms of information on the internet that might also be helpful. The main thing to be mindful of when gathering information, is the quality of the information and the age of the information. One should ensure any information gathered is from a reputable and professional source. The information should also be current, because the issues with HIV/AIDS are constantly changing.

Once the six individual areas of life have been examined it is important that the individual continues to examine each of the areas on an ongoing basis. Life issues, relationships and mental and physical conditions are ever changing, as well as diagnoses, medications, and research.

Before starting this self examination it is a good idea to get a large notebook with labeled sections to help one to keep notes and become organized. There is no particular order to address these areas. What may be of primary importance to one person may be secondary to another. As the individual goes through the six areas they should write about their thoughts, feelings, important data, behaviors, goals, and progress. This book should become a very valuable and personal tool to help the individual stay focused and current with what is really important to their mental and physical health.

PHYSICAL/MEDICAL HEALTH AREA OF LIFE

In this area the individual must take time to evaluate all aspects of their physical health. Because HIV/AIDS is a biological disease that can seriously impact one's physical health, this area must come first. The individual should get a good check-up from their doctor.

The patient should get the results from any tests that were taken and ask what the information means.They should write down any and all medications and the instructions for those medications. They should also write down any instructions from the doctor or nurse with regard to self-care, nutrition, exercise, and habits. If the doctor does not address these areas, then it is the responsibility of the patient to ask.

When gathering information, the cleint should always write down the date, name, and phone number of the person they talked to in case they have more questions later. If for some reason the individual has trouble understanding or writing, they should ask the professional to write the information down for them. This type of information should be gathered on every doctor's visit and telephone conversation. It can be a very useful tool for day-to-day health care management, as well as a good tracking tool to keep up with progress and presenting concerns or problems. It should be used to write down the first signs of possible side effects and visible body changes. It should also be used to keep track of the things that are working and helping. Documentation is very important for many reasons:

a. For many African Americans the shame of having HIV/AIDS is so overwhelming that they are anxious to get out of the office for fear of being seen. In their haste and fear, they may not be paying attention or be willing to stay long enough to get all of the information needed.

b. For many African Americans, especially those with limited education, medical terminology may be confusing and difficult to comprehend. They may feel intimidated and at the mercy of the professional, and therefore less likely to ask questions or get clarification.

c. Unfortunately, professionals make mistakes too. It is always better to have accurate information just in case something goes wrong with the instructions, medication, or information.

d. Having HIV/AIDS, as well as all of the other possible concerns of life, can be very emotional. For many, just going to the doctor's office can stir up a lot of feelings that may be blocking the individual's comprehension of what is going on.

The object of this whole section is to help the individual take an active and responsible part in the medical aspects of their life and to help those who need self-empowerment within the medical system.

THE EMOTIONAL/ SPIRITUAL AREA OF LIFE

This area helps the individual analyze the mental health aspects of their life. These aspects include such items as emotions, feelings, stress, and inner-growth, as well as faith, beliefs, and spirituality.

Once again it is important for the individual to keep up with any of these issues that may be causing some concern. Sometimes just writing about one's feelings helps them to sort things out and gain a better understanding. If any of these feelings are frequently reoccurring, overwhelming, or out of control, it may be necessary to ask for professional help. If emotional problems are serious, they can cause physical health problems and thereby compromise ones HIV/AIDS status.

Such emotional issues as depression, stress, and anger can be both mentally and physically unhealthy. For many African Americans, particularly those who have been dealing with these feelings even before HIV/AIDS, such emotions can often be underestimated or overlooked simply because the individual may "think it is a normal way of life." It is not unusual for African Americans to become almost "accepting" of one stress after another, without ever realizing that there may be ways to reduce its effects on the body and the mind.

For the very religious and/or spiritual African American, getting involved with their church or religion can be extremely helpful. If their pastor or church is not accommodating or helpful, then perhaps it is necessary for that individual to find a more sensitive and responsive arena to practice their belief system.

Historically, African Americans have been very religious people and prayer has been very important. Therefore, even if an individual does not have a comfort level with a particular church or religious institution they can still practice their faith and belief system alone or with a select group of friends and family.

Many churches and congregations are now becoming sensitive and responsive to HIV/AIDS. These types of churches and people can be very supportive, caring, and comforting to an individual who is struggling with life and life issues.

Whether the individual should choose to seek professional or spiritual help, the notebook is still a good tool to keep information. The notebook is a good place to keep advice from professionals, mental health books, motivational books, prayers, spiritual messages, or spiritual songs that have been uplifting to the individual.

BEHAVIORAL AREA OF LIFE

The behavioral area of life stresses the need for African Americans to properly address and control addictive and destructive behaviors that may have developed in their lives. These behaviors include alcohol and substance abuse, smoking, unsafe sexual practices, sexual promiscuity, and other obsessive or compulsive behaviors such as overeating, lying, and manipulating.

This is probably the most difficult of the areas of life to change, often interrelated with all of the other areas of life. Professional help such as behavioral therapy, substance abuse recovery programs, or medical assistance may be needed to work through some of these practices. But they must be addressed and changed appropriately.

Continued unhealthy and addictive behaviors will only add to the physical and emotional problems that an individual with HIV/AIDS has to deal with. Some of these behaviors do not mix well with medication, medical therapy, or mental health therapy.

If an individual really cares about the quality of life and living a positive and healthy life, then they have to be willing to make some serious behavioral changes. It does little good to follow the doctor's orders, adhere to medication and pray daily, if the individual is also excessively drinking or using non-prescription drugs.

These behavioral problems are often coupled with emotional ones. Professional counseling is a good place to perhaps work with any of these issues simultaneously. The notebook is a good place to start tracking any of these inappropriate behaviors.

Many African Americans, because of oppression and depression, do not even realize these behaviors are excessive. Keep track of the amount of money and time spent, the people affected and how they are affected, the way the individual feels before and after the behavior, and how the behavior is affecting their physical and mental health.

<u>MATERIAL NEEDS</u>
<u>AREA OF LIFE</u>

For some African Americans, particularly those who are at lower socio-economic levels, this may be the priority area to address. It is very difficult to care about medication or depression if an individual is worried about having a roof over their head, safety, food and clothing, or adequate child care. Most African Americans are willing to work but may need help in finding a job. However, for some African Americans with HIV/AIDS, their health problems may require that they stay at home and not work. Therefore they may need financial assistance.

These issues must be addressed in order for anyone to concentrate on the other areas of life. Fortunately for individuals with HIV/AIDS, there are various programs and services in most larger counties and cities available to assist them with some of these needs. However, it is the individual's responsibility to inquire, and, if need be, get help in accessing these programs and services.

Professional help may be needed from a social worker or a case manager from an HIV/AIDS agency or service provider. For many African Americans this can be a difficult issue to address. Many individuals are struggling with pride and shame and are resistant to accepting what is often thought of as charity. And for others who have been mistreated by social or government services in the past, there may be feelings of fear and mistrust that keep them from seeking such help. It is important to note that, if indeed an individual decides to seek professional help, they need to be honest and sincere in their needs and their data.

The notebook is a good place to list the various agencies, professionals, names and numbers. It is a good place to do an assessment of needs to find out what is available and how one can get their needs met. Often, applications have to be completed or forms have to be filed. Results are often slow to receive, so patience and time may be needed. Getting material or financial help is not to be used as a tool to abuse the available services or available funds, but is one to be used for those who are in serious need. Once their basic survival needs are met, they are better able to focus on their mental and physical health care.

The purpose of addressing this area of life is for individuals to properly gain and maintain adequate levels of financial assistance, while controlling financial responsibility and staying focused on what is important for their survival and quality of life.

FAMILY/SOCIAL AREA OF LIFE

The African American family is usually very strong and influential. This type of family can be a positive attribute, but it can also be a negative liability. For many reasons, African American family and social systems can be coupled with great love and care as well as serious pains and problems that are repeated for generations.

For an African American with HIV/AIDS, family and social support can be very needed and helpful. These individuals can greatly benefit from a strong and reliable support system they can trust and depend on. Having someone to talk to and share with can make a great difference in how one adjusts to HIV/AIDS. Acceptance by loved ones is very important to many of these individuals. Family members need to be non-judgmental, supportive and sensitive to the needs of the person with HIV/AIDS. They must also take it upon themselves to educate themselves so they are able to provide adequate assistance when needed.

Should the individual with HIV/AIDS have a very troubled and difficult family, then that individual must do what is best for themselves by perhaps avoiding the stress or ills that the family may provide. Because of the emotional components of family relationships, the stress can be overwhelming and harmful to one's mental and physical well being. If a person is fighting substance abuse and the family is using drugs, then it is perfectly understandable if that individual chooses to stay away from their family, in order to remain clean and sober.

If the family is unavailable or unsupportive, there are other avenues that are available such as support groups, church groups and HIV/AIDS-related workshops, conferences, or seminars. These are usually positive avenues for finding supportive people. Even just a few select friends to talk to and confide in will be better than dealing with HIV/AIDS alone and isolated.

Individuals from strong and influential families, positive or negative, will have to learn to set appropriate boundaries with the family members. Over protective families can inhibit an individuals ability to become proactive and responsible for their own health care.

The notebook can be used to list the names and numbers of the positive and supportive people in one's life. These are the people, whether they are family or friends, who the person with HIV/AIDS can lean on or trust. The notebook can also be used to list the people that cause stress or problems in an individual's life. These are the people the person with HIV/AIDS should either avoid or learn to deal with on a healthy basis.

Families can also trigger emotions such as grief, anger, resentment and depression about things that may have happened to the individual with HIV/AIDS as a child.

These are some of the issues that can be addressed with a good psychologist or licensed counselor.

Telling family members of one's HIV/AIDS diagnosis or health status can be difficult. It is usually best to tell only those individuals who they feel have a need and or right to know. For some individuals this may mean parents, to others, it may mean children. The important thing to understand is that people who love the individual with HIV/AIDS are also impacted by what happens to them. Informing children, when need-be, can also be difficult. The children need to be able to understand in order to effectively deal with the information the individual with HIV/AIDS is disclosing. The parent must also be able to deal with the same disclosure issues. If the parent is still struggling, then it may make things even more difficult for the child.

Yet another issue to be examined is that of the young children of adults who have HIV/AIDS. Parents at some time or another may have to investigate the options for the care of their children, should they become seriously ill or die. This is a reality some parents must face. Again, the various HIV/AIDS agencies should be of some assistance in these areas with respect to any legal documentation that might have to be developed.

INTIMATE/SEXUAL AREA OF LIFE

The intimate/sexual area of life needs to be addressed separately from that of the family/social area of life because the types of relationships are very different.

This is an area of life that often causes the most distress for adults living with HIV/AIDS. Because of the complex sexuality component of HIV/AIDS, intimate and sexual relationships can become very difficult to face.

One of the issues the person with HIV/AIDS needs to address is the disclosure of their HIV/AIDS status. He or she must consider informing any individual who they have possibly exposed to the virus, and encourage them to be tested. Disclosure of HIV/AIDS status can be very difficult and sometimes dangerous, depending on the parties involved.

Everyone who has been put at-risk should be tested, not only to help the individual with getting treatment, but to help stop the spread of the disease to others. If for some reason the person with HIV/AIDS does not want to tell the other party or they don't want the other party to know who they are, there are various anonymous reporting services available throughout most county health departments. Nevertheless, effort needs to be made to get individual's who have been put at-risk tested for HIV/AIDS.

Another issue to be considered is disclosure of HIV/AIDS status to individuals before becoming intimate with them. Many individuals with HIV/AIDS struggle with telling prospective lovers, for fear of rejection which is very hurtful. No one wants to go through that emotion. However, putting someone's health and life at risk should take precedence over these feelings.

Again, disclosure should be given to individuals who need to know. If an individual with HIV/AIDS is considering becoming intimate with another individual, that party needs to know. Sexual promiscuity is dangerous, but it is also dangerous having unprotected sex.

-The notebook is a good place to write down any thoughts, feelings, and if need be, a list of individuals who need to be contacted. When the person with HIV/AIDS is thinking and trying to make a decision, it is perfectly all right to seek professional help in working through some of the decisions. The notebook is also a good place to write about how the individual is feeling before and after any action has been taken.

Intimate relationships can be very supportive and comforting, but they can also be very stressful, unhappy and unhealthy. If the relationship the individual is in is also stressful and non-supportive, it can be difficult to have quality of life. Making some changes in the structure of the relationship may become necessary in order for the individuals to have a happier life.

Many African Americans who have HIV/AIDS are also homosexual or bisexual. The African American community is not as accepting of these sexual preferences as the White community. There may be a host of issues regarding sexuality and sexual identity that may be affecting the quality of life for some African Americans. These are all issues that should be dealt, and perhaps along with a professional.

Until African Americans can talk about and face homosexuality, while learning to deal with it as a part of their life, there may always be some hidden fears and anxiety to impede one's quality of life. "Coming out of the closet," is an individual decision, and it is not always the best decision, but there is nothing wrong with getting help with that decision, whatever it may be.

CONCLUSION

The quality of life is all encompassing, requiring one to really do deep and sincere inner-work. That work will require time, patience and commitment. Add the components of being African American with HIV/AIDS and the work is even harder. But it can happen. The important thing to remember is that it doesn't have to happen without assistance.

Today there are many African American individuals diagnosed with HIV/AIDS who are living full and happy lives. It is not always easy, but it can and does happen. When all of these areas of life are addressed, explored and improved upon, the individual with HIV/AIDS should begin to establish some solid ground work for self-development and inner growth. When these issues are dealt with properly, the individual with HIV/AIDS should begin to feel better about themselves, self-esteem should grow, and they should begin to be responsible and honest with oneself and others. The notebook is designed to give individuals a forum to document vital information as well as face thoughts and feelings about themselves. Individuals will learn to admit and change negative characteristics while developing self-love.

REFERENCES

Achterberg, J., & Lawlis, G.F. (1990). <u>Health Attribution test: User's guide.</u> In Randall S. Bergen (Ed.), Institute for Personality and Ability Testing, Inc., Champaign, Ill: Institute for Personality and Ability Testing, Inc.

Aoki, B.K. (1989). Cross-cultural counseling: The extra dimension. In J.W. Dilley, C. Pies, & M. Helquist (Eds.), <u>Face to Face.</u> (pp. 26-33). San Francisco, CA: AIDS Health Project.

Belgrave, F.Z., & Randolph S.M. (1993). Psychosocial aspects of AIDS prevention among African Americans. <u>The Journal of Black Psychology, 19,</u> 103-107.

Belgrave, F.Z., Randolph S.M., Carter, C., Braithwaite, N., & Arrington, T. (1993). The impact of knowledge, norms, and self-efficacy on intentions to engage in AIDS-preventive behaviors among young incarcerated African American males. <u>The Journal of Black Psychology, 19,</u> 155-168.

AIDS &
African Americans

Blackwell, P., (1994). African American Homosexual/bisexual Males and the Human Immunodeficiency Virus/Acquired Immune Deficiency Syndrome: A Study of Racial Identity and Health Care Attribution. East Texas State University, Commerce, Texas

Carter, R.T., & Helms J.E. (1987). The relationship of black value-orientations to racial identity attitudes. Measurement and Evaluation in Counseling and Development, 19, 185-195.

Centers for Disease Control and Prevention. (1999). HIV/AIDS Surveillance Report (Vol. 11, No. 1). Atlanta, GA: Division of HIV/AIDS, National Center for Infectious Diseases.

Centers for Disease Control and Prevention. (1998). HIV/AIDS Surveillance Report (Vol. 10, No. 1). Atlanta, GA: Division of HIV/AIDS, National Center for Infectious Diseases.

Centers for Disease Control and Prevention. (1997). HIV/AIDS Surveillance Report (Vol.9, No. 1). Atlanta, GA: Division of HIV/AIDS, National Center for Infectious Diseases.

Centers for Disease Control and Prevention. (1997). HIV/AIDS Surveillance Report (Vol.8, No. 2). Atlanta, GA: Division of HIV/AIDS, National Center for Infectious Diseases.

Cochran, S.D., & Mays, V.M. (1993). Applying social psychological models to predicting HIV-related sexual risk behaviors among African Americans. Journal of Black Psychology, 19, 142-154.

Cross, W.E., Jr. (1971). The negro-to-black conversion experience. Black World, 20(9), 12-27.

Cross, W.E., Jr. (1978). Models of psychological nigrescence: A literature review. Journal of Black Psychology, 5(1), 12-31.

Cross, W.E., Jr. (1980). Models of psychological nigrescence: A literature review. In R.L. Jones (Ed.), Black Psychology (pp. 81-98). New York: Harper & Row.

Croteau, J.M., Morgan, S., Henderson, B., & Nero, C.I. (1992). Race, gender, and sexual orientation in the HIV/AIDS epidemic: Evaluating an intervention for leaders of diverse communities. Journal of Multicultural Counseling and Development, 20, 168-180).

Croteau, J.M., Nero, C.I., & Prosser, D.J. (1993). Social and cultural sensitivity in group-specific HIV and AIDS programming. Journal of Counseling & Development, 71, 290-296.

Dalton, H.L. (1989). AIDS in blackface. Daedalus, 118(3), 205-227.

Forward, J.R., & Williams, J.R. (1970). Internal-external control and Black militancy. The Journal of Social Issues, 26, No. 1, 75-92.

Foster, P., Phillips, F., Belgrave, F.Z., Randolph, S.M., & Braithwaite, N. (1993). An Africentric model for AIDS education, prevention, and psychological services within the African American community. Journal of Black Psychology, 19, 123-141.

Fullilove, M.T. (1989). Ethnic minorities, HIV disease and the growing underclass. In J.W. Dilley, C. Pies, & M. Helquist (Eds.), Face to Face (pp. 230-240). San Francisco, CA: AIDS Health Project.

Goodwin, N.J. (1992). AIDS & African-Americans: It's time for action. Crisis, 100, 16-18 & 72.

Hall, W.S., Cross W.E., Jr., & Freedle, R. (1972). Stages in the development of black awareness: An exploratory investigation. In R.L. Jones (Ed.), Black Psychology. (pp. 156-165). New York: Harper & Row.

Heider, F. (1958). The psychology of interpersonal relations. New York: Wiley.

Helms, J.E. (1984). Toward a theoretical explanation of the effects of race on counseling: A Black and White model. The Counseling Psychologist, 12(4), 153-165.

Helms, J. E. (1987). Cultural identity in the treatment process. In P.B. Pedersen (Ed.), <u>Handbook of cross-cultural counseling and psychotherapy</u> (pp. 239-245). Westport, CT: Greenwood Press.

Helms, J.E. (1989). Considering some methodological issues in racial identity counseling research. <u>The Counseling Psychologist, 17,</u> 227-252.

Helms, J.E. (1993). <u>Black and White racial identity: Theory, research, and practice.</u> Westport, CT: Praeger.

Jackson, B. (1975). Black identity development. <u>Journal of Educational Diversity & Innovation, 2,</u> 19-25.

Jenkins, B., Lamar, V.L., & Thompson-Crumble, J., (1993). AIDS among African Americans: A social epidemic. <u>The Journal of Black Psychology, 19,</u> 108-122.

Jue, S., & Kain C.D. (1989). Culturally sensitive AIDS counseling. In C.D. Kain (Ed.), <u>No Longer Immune: A Counselor's Guide to AIDS.</u> (pp. 131-148). Alexandria, VA: American Association for Counseling and Development.

Lefcourt, H.M. (1982). <u>Locus of control: Current trends in theory and research</u> (2nd ed.), Hillsdale, NJ: Erlbaum.

Lester, C. & Saxxon, L.L. (1988). AIDS in the black community: The plague, the politics, the people. Death Studies, 12, 563-571.

Mitchell, A. (1990). AIDS: We are not immune. Emerge, 2, 30-44.

National Institute of Allergy and Infectious Diseases, (1997). Minorities and HIV Infection. National Institutes of Health.

Parham, T.A., & Helms, J.E. (1981). Influence of a Black student's racial identity attitudes on preference for a counselor race. Journal of Counseling Psychology, 28, 250-257.

Phares, E.J. (1976). Locus of control in personality. Morristown, N.J.: General Learning Press.

Ramseur, H.P. (1989). Psychologically health black adults: A review of theory and research. In R.L. Jones (Ed.), Black Adult Development and Aging (pp. 215-241). Berkeley, CA: Cobb & Henry.

Rotter, J.B. (1954). Social learning and clinical psychology. Englewood Cliffs, NJ: Prentice-Hall.

Rotter, J.B. (1966). Generalized expectancies for internal versus external control of reinforce ment. Psychological Monograph, 80, Whole no. 69.

Rotter, J.B. (1982). <u>The development and application of social learning theory:</u> Selected Paper. New York: Praeger Publishers.

Sue, D.W., & Sue, D. (1990). Racial/cultural identity development. In D.W. Sue & D. Sue (Eds.), <u>Counseling the Culturally Different</u> (pp. 93-117). New York: John Wiley & Sons.

Terrell, F., (1995). <u>Characteristics Common Among African-American Clients</u>: Selected Paper. University of North Texas.

Terrell, F., & Terrell, S.L. (1981). An inventory to measure cultural mistrust among blacks, <u>Western Journal of Black Studies, 5.</u>

Thomas, C.W. (1971). <u>Boys no more</u>. Beverly Hills, CA: Glencoe Press.

Thomas, S.B., & Quinn, S.C. (1991). The Tuskegee syphilis study, 1932 to 1972: Implications for HIV education and AIDS risk reduction in the Black community. <u>American Journal of Public Health, 81</u>, (11), 1498-1505.

AIDS &
African Americans

NCD PUBLISHING
Order Form

For U.S. orders, please include $3.00 postage and handling for the first books ordered, and $1.00 for each additional book. Orders outside USA, send money order payable in US dollars on US Bank only.

Name _____

Address _____

City _____ State_____ ZIP _____

Quantity	Price	Total
	21.95	

	Subtotal	_____
	Postage and Handling	_____
	Texas residents add 8.25%	_____
	Total	_____

Make checks payable to NCD

Mail to: Nia Consulting & Development
       P.O. Box 741594
       Dallas, Texas 75374-1594

Phone orders to: 1-800-484-9410
       Security code # 4660

Accept Am. Ex., Master Card & Visa